Early ADVENT SINGING

James R. Nix

A collection of 52
early Adventist hymns
with illustrating stories

A revision and enlargement of
Advent Singing

Review and Herald®
Publishing Association
Hagerstown, MD 21740

Copyright © 1994
Review and Herald® Publishing Association

The author assumes full responsibility for the accuracy
of all facts and quotations as cited in this book.

This book was
Edited by Raymond H. Woolsey
Designed by Helcio Deslandes
Cover design by Byron Steele
Type set: 12/14 Goudy

PRINTED IN U.S.A.

98 97 96 95 94   10 9 8 7 6 5 4 3 2 1

Library of Congress Cataloging in Publication Data
Early Advent singing :   a collection of 52 early Adventist hymns with
    illustrating stories / [compiled] by James R. Nix.
    1 close score.
    Rev. and enl. ed. of: Advent singing. © 1988.

    1. Adventists—United States—Hymns.   2. Seventh-day Adventists—United
States—Hymns.   3. Hymns, English.   4. Adventists—United States—Hymns—
History and criticism.   I. Nix, James R.   II. Advent singing.
M2131.A3E37   1994   94-30720
                                                              CIP
                                                               M

ISBN 0-8280-0892-2

DEDICATION

To
My daughter, Shannon Nix,
who shares with me an
enthusiasm for early
Advent singing

ACKNOWLEDGMENTS

(For the first edition)

S everal people assisted in the preparation of *Advent Singing*. I want to express my appreciation to each of them.

To Ron Graybill I owe a debt of gratitude. He was the first to interest me in the story of our early Adventist hymns beyond those found in the 1941 *Church Hymnal*. By so doing, he has enriched my life immeasurably. In addition, his research into this area proved a rich resource as I worked on this book.

When I first approached Wayne Hooper about background information for my book, he generously made available a draft copy of several portions of the book that he and Edward E. White coauthored, *Companion to the Seventh-day Adventist Hymnal*, which was then in preparation. He also read the manuscript and offered valuable suggestions. Likewise, Louise Dederen, of the Adventist Heritage Center at Andrews University, was most helpful. She supplied copies of several Seventh-day Adventist hymnals not otherwise available to me. And Sandra Gregory Gray, vocal soloist and voice teacher of Chicago, Illinois, kindly assisted with several of the tune arrangements that are used in the book.

I am especially appreciative of those who read the manuscript and shared their suggestions with me. Besides the ones mentioned, there were Paul A. Gordon and Esther Ramharacksingh Knott, both of the General Conference, as well as Peter Hart and Beverly Koester, of the Heritage Room at Loma Linda University. My thanks also to Beverly Rumble, who copyedited the manuscript. Assisting me with the selection of tunes were Catherine Miller and Dave and Alma Rios.

A special word of appreciation to my secretary, Shirley Chipman, who typed and retyped the manuscript. Her enthusiasm for the project from its beginning, even at times when I wondered if I would ever complete the book, was contagious.

Finally, I want to express my appreciation to my daughter, Shannon Nix. She put up with my humming and singing of early Adventist hymns around the home during the weeks I was writing the manuscript and deciding for certain which songs to include in *Advent Singing*.

James R. Nix
April 20, 1988
Loma Linda, California

ACKNOWLEDGMENTS

(For the second edition)

For some time many people have wanted to buy copies of *Advent Singing*, the first edition of this book, but none have been available. That initial printing was produced by the North American Division Office of Education for use by elementary and secondary teachers. No copies were printed for public sale. Consequently, when the Review and Herald Publishing Association approached me about reprinting the book, I was fully in agreement with the idea. However, I did want to correct several mistakes in the first edition, as well as replace several of the hymns with different ones in a revised and expanded second edition.

A few additional individuals have assisted me in the preparation of this new edition of *Early Advent Singing*. I want to express my appreciation to each of them.

Among these are Al and Geraldine Hess. Not only did they assist in determining which hymns to retain and which to change from the first edition, but they also helped with the selection of some of the hymn tunes.

Most especially I want to thank my wife, Mindi, for her help. She volunteered to retype the entire manuscript, and also helped with the selection of hymns included in this new edition. Since my daughter, Shannon, is now off to college, it was Mindi who heard me singing early Adventist hymns around home during the weeks I was working on revising the manuscript. Without her assistance, this new edition of *Early Advent Singing* would never have become a reality.

James R. Nix
March 27, 1994
Laurel, Maryland

CONTENTS

Early Seventh-day Adventist Hymns—1863-1915

MILLERITE
ADVENTIST HYMNS

1841-1844

MILLERITE ADVENTIST HYMNS

I t is a fact that there was in those days a power in what was called Advent singing, such as was felt in no other." So wrote James White in *Life Incidents*, his autobiography published in 1868, as he reflected on the singing done during the Millerite Adventist movement of 25 years earlier.

Since originally the Millerites remained in their own churches, most likely they sang from the hymnals of their various denominations. But after they began holding meetings of their own, and especially after the introduction of the Great Tent in the summer of 1842, apparently they found it desirable to produce their own hymnals.

The first move in that direction was the publication of three hymns in the June 15, 1841, issue of the Millerite *Signs of the Times and Expositor of Prophecy*. In that same issue, there was also a notice recommending the purchase of *The Vestry Singing Book*, published in Boston.

About six weeks later, the following announcement appeared in the *Signs of the Times*:

> SONGS OF ZION. A small volume of the *Songs of Zion* is in preparation and will be published soon; suited to the wants of Second Advent Conference meetings and Bible classes. Any persons having appropriate hymns which they would like to have inserted will greatly oblige us by sending them to the editor of this paper without delay.

In the October 1, 1841, issue of the *Signs of the Times*, another announcement appeared:

> Millennial Musings
> A selection of soul-stirring hymns and spiritual songs, from various authors, relative to the return of the Lord, and the preparation of His saints to meet Him in peace. It is designed for Second Advent meetings for prayer and conference. It will be out the 8th of October.

Apparently the name of the new hymnal had been changed

during the weeks between the first and second announcements. As with many projects, this one took longer to complete than originally anticipated. In the November 1, 1841, issue of the *Signs of the Times* another notice appeared. It too stated that the new hymnal would "be out the 8th of October." Already three weeks late at that time, it was not until the January 1, 1842, issue of the paper that the following announcement appeared:

> HYMN BOOKS. "Millennial Musings.—A choice selection of hymns designed for the use of Second Advent Meetings." By J. V. Himes and J. Litch. Price $2.40 per dozen, 20 cents single.

Millennial Musings: A Choice Selection of Hymns Designed for the Use of Second Advent Meetings contained the words only for 121 hymns on 144 pages; it had no music.

In the July 27, 1842, issue of the Millerite paper *Signs of the Times*, Joshua V. Himes placed a notice about a new hymnal that would be available in a few days. It contained two parts bound together: the *Millennial Harp, or Second Advent Hymns; Designed for Meetings on the Second Coming of Christ*, consisting of 72 pages, and a reprint of *Millennial Musings*. The price was 37 ½ cents in cloth binding, or the two sections could be bought individually. Priced separately, the first part was 12 ½ cents and the second part was 17 cents in paper or 20 cents hardbound. The combined hymnal is generally referred to as the 1842 *Millennial Harp*. As would be expected, the hymns were predominately about the second coming of Christ. A total of 169 songs appeared in the book. In the first part there was music with the words, while the second section still had words only.

The Millerites also produced a small throwaway-type evangelistic hymnal called *Second Advent Hymns: Designed to Be Used in Prayer and Camp-Meetings*, published in 1842 by Joshua V. Himes. This small book, just three inches by four inches, contained 19 hymns printed on 32 pages. It had no music, just the words. This small hymnal may have been produced for use in the Great Tent (see description under "Together Let Us Sweetly Live") as well as at Millerite camp meetings.

In 1843 an expanded throwaway-type hymnal of 64 pages, described as a "new edition," was offered for sale at the same price as the 1842 booklet—6¼ cents each. Also in 1843, an "improved edition" of *Millennial Harp, Designed for Meetings on the Second Coming of Christ* was published by Himes. It consisted of three parts. Subsequent editions with 36-page or 72-page supplements were also published. The original book contained a total of 213 hymns. Two of its three sections contained music with the words. If preferred, a person could also buy the first two parts as separate pamphlets. They were numbers 23 and 37 of the "Second Advent Library," a series of tracts that Himes also published.

Reports from the time contain several accounts of Millerite singing. On one occasion, Joseph Bates, a Millerite who later became one of the cofounders of the Seventh-day Adventist Church, found himself, along with some other Adventists, forced to wait several hours in a train station in Salem, Massachusetts. The group filled the time while awaiting the next train by "singing Advent hymns." This was something new to the people of Salem, who "came out in crowds, and seemed to listen with breathless attention." The singing caused enough interest that Silas Hawley, a preacher who had just accepted Millerism, was invited to preach on the subject the next Sunday. An estimated crowd of 7,000 turned out to hear him.

The Millerite camp meetings were also noted for their singing. In fact, as the participants came to the closing day, the parting campers marched in joyful ranks around the camp while singing an Advent hymn. Then followed the farewell handclasp that symbolized their deep sense of fellowship and the submerging of "sectarian prejudices," as another impressive camp meeting had ended.

The Millerites' hymns included a combination of religious folk songs as well as pieces that were influenced by the churches from which they originally had come. The 1985 *Seventh-day Adventist Hymnal* contains 20 hymns (listed below) that were included in the Millerite hymnals besides those chosen for *Early Advent Singing*. In some cases the tunes used in the 1985 *Hymnal* have been changed or the words altered somewhat from what the Millerites originally sang. The hymns in this list also illustrate the variety of song types that were known to the Millerites.

---

* Millerites sang this hymn as "Must Simon bear his cross alone?" The words were considerably altered throughout the hymn, and the tune was different. The original words and tune were also used in Seventh-day Adventist hymnals as late as *Hymns and Tunes*, published in 1886, No. 1173.

ANGELS HOVERING ROUND

E llen White found comfort in songs that breathed assurance of heavenly companionship. According to her oldest granddaughter, Ella (White) Robinson, this little chorus was one of her grandmother's favorites. Mrs. White often would hum or sing it as she went about her work during the day.

Even though all of us have guardian angels, we do not normally see them. During Ellen White's lifetime she often was visited by an angel, despite the fact that those people around her generally were unaware of the angel's presence. However, there were a few rare exceptions when others also were privileged to see the angel.

On one occasion, possibly January 1, 1881 (the exact date is not now known for certain), James White picked up his ill wife, Ellen, in his arms and took her out to their waiting carriage. Mrs. White was sick with a cold and could talk only in a whisper, but she had a speaking appointment that evening at the Dime Tabernacle in Battle Creek, Michigan. (For the story of how the church acquired its unusual name, see under "We Know Not the Time When He Cometh.")

In the audience that evening were two college girls, Ella King and Edith Donaldson. Ella had not yet joined the Seventh-day Adventist Church, but was attending Battle Creek College because her mother had become a member. Her friend Edith had traveled with the Whites as they had come from Oregon to Michigan. That evening, though, Edith was resentful as she saw Ellen White struggle to speak in a barely audible voice. Mrs. White hung onto the pulpit, trying to steady herself as she spoke, but only a few in the front rows could hear her. Edith felt bitter toward a God who would force Ellen White to strain so hard to be heard when so many prayers had been offered asking that she be healed. As Edith sat there, she wondered to herself how she could ever serve such an unjust God. And try as hard as Ellen White might, her message that night was just not getting through because of her illness.

"Suddenly 'something like an electric shock went through Edith Donaldson, and she trembled all over. Then she saw a light of dazzling brightness which seemed to be entering the building through an opening in the ceiling. . . . At the same time Ella King's attention was attracted to the gallery window at the left, nearest the pulpit, where the light moved like the waving of wings. Simultaneously, the two girls nudged each other, whispering, "An angel."

" 'The brilliant light passed overhead, directly to Mrs. White, who stood leaning on the pulpit. It enveloped her, and then everything on the rostrum was hidden from the sight of those two girls. They were blinded by the brightness for some moments. When they could see again, the light had vanished, and Mrs. White stood strong and erect at the edge of the rostrum, holding her Bible in one hand. Her voice pealed out like a bell, and her first words were, "God has sent His angel and strengthened me." Ellen went on speaking for over an hour in her usual stirring voice. . . . God had healed Ellen. . . . Later that same evening James White asked Edith, 'Did you see the angel?'

"She replied that she had.

" 'Thank the Lord,' he said, 'that He opened your eyes. He did it for a purpose.'

"Mary Kelsey White, Willie's wife, and James had also seen the light, as it covered Ellen.

" 'All who were in that large congregation saw the work of healing that was performed, but as far as could be ascertained, only those four were privileged to behold that brilliant demonstration.

" 'What they saw they could never forget. Edith felt that she had been a faithless, doubting Thomas, and that the Lord in mercy had awakened her to a new life. She and Ella were baptized, and as Edith Donaldson Brownsberger and Ella King Sanders they have both lived long lives of usefulness in the service of the Master' " (Paul B. Ricchiuti, *Ellen*, pp. 122-124).

The chorus "Angels Hovering Round" first appeared in Joshua V. Himes's 1843 edition of the *Millennial Harp*, designed for use by the Millerite Adventists. James White picked up the chorus and included it in his 1855 and 1861 hymnals. It was republished again in the "Miscellaneous—Old Melodies" section of the 1886 *Hymns and Tunes*. The last Adventist hymnal to include this chorus was *Christ in Song*, copyrighted in 1908. All the stanzas as first printed by Himes are included in *Second Advent Singing*.

Angels Hovering Round

From Millenial Harp, *1843*

Arr. from Millenial Harp, *1843*

1. There are an-gels hov-'ring round, There are an - gels hov-'ring round,
2. To car - ry ti - dings home, To car - ry ti - dings home,
3. To the new Je - ru - sa - lem: To the new Je - ru - sa - lem:

There are an - gels, an - gels hov - 'ring round.
To car - ry, car - ry ti - dings home.
To the New, the New - Je - ru - sa - lem.

4. Poor sinners are coming home,
5. And Jesus bids them come;
6. Let him that heareth come,
7. Let him that thirsteth come,
8. We are on our journey home,

9. Where Christ our Lord has gone;
10. We will meet around His throne,
11. When He makes His people one,
12. We shall reign forevermore,
13. In the New Jerusalem.

HERE IS NO REST

The early Millerites felt the sting of alienation as the churches to which they had belonged disfellowshipped them. Their hope was in the promised world to come rather than in their citizenship of this earth. "Here Is No Rest" spoke of those feelings.

Later, when the Sabbath truth was discovered, the early believers found that this hymn again described their experience. To keep the Sabbath was not easy while all their neighbors worked that day, nor, for that matter, was it easy for them to work in their own yards or fields on Sundays as everyone else drove by in their buggies headed to church. Such circumstances tended to cause our pioneers to feel that they were out of step with their society. And the fact that Seventh-day Adventists were few in number and relatively unknown only compounded the problem. At the founding of the General Conference in 1863 there were only approximately 3,500 members, scattered mainly throughout the northeastern United States. Even by 1886, the year of the last Seventh-day Adventist hymnal to include this hymn, the number of church members had grown to only 23,111.

This particular hymn was mentioned by Hiram Edson in his handwritten autobiographical statement recounting his Millerite experiences. Sometime during what was called the seventh-month movement—that period of time just before October 22, 1844— Edson and some friends were busy passing out literature in the daytime and holding meetings at night. One evening, just as they were about to start their service, a two-horse wagon full of total strangers pulled up. Edson and his friends quickly prepared seats for the newcomers, after which the meeting was opened by singing, "Here o'er the earth as a stranger I roam; here is no rest, is no rest."

Edson recalled, "It was sung with the spirit and with the understanding, and the spirit which accompanied the singing gave to it a keen edge." Before the hymn even had been completely sung through, the group of newcomers came under such conviction that rather than face the embarrassment of having to admit they had been converted at a Millerite meeting, they all decided to leave. But though they started for the door of the house, only one man and his wife actually went out. The other 13 became so affected by what they were hearing they remained and were converted before the meeting closed that evening.

The couple who had gone outside tried to get the others in their group to leave also. Failing to do so, they decided to walk the five or six miles home, carrying their 1-year-old child with them. This seemed better to them than having to stay at a Millerite meeting.

Hiram Edson concluded his account by saying, "But [the child] was not their heaviest burden. Their conviction was too deep to be easily shaken off; they were back again at the next evening meeting and found pardon and peace in believing."

The hymn "Here Is No Rest" was included in both the 36-page and later the 72-page *Supplement* to the 1843 edition of the Millerite hymnal, the *Millennial Harp*, produced by Joshua V. Himes. James White later included it in his 1849 hymnal, entitled *Hymns for God's Peculiar People That Keep the Commandments of God and the Faith of Jesus*. The hymn was retained in our hymnals through *Hymns and Tunes*, first published in 1886.

The original tune, which is used here, is LONG, LONG AGO. However, the hymn also works very nicely with another early Advent hymn tune, HOMEWARD BOUND, which can be found in the 1941 *Church Hymnal*, No. 661.

Here Is No Rest

From Millenial Harp, *1843*

LONG, LONG AGO

1. Here o'er the earth as a strang-er I roam,
2. Here fierce tempta-tion be-set me a-round;
3. Here are af-flic-tions and tri-als se-vere;
4. This world of cares is a wil-der-ness state,

Here is no rest, is no rest;

Here as a pil-grim I wan-der a-lone,
Here I am grieved while my foes me sur-round;
Here I must part with the friends I hold dear;
Here I must bear from the world all its hate,

Yet I am blest, I am blest.

For I look forward to that glorious day, When sin and sorrow will van-ish a-way.
Let them re-vile me and scoff at my name, Laugh at my weeping, en-deav-or to shame;
Sweet is the prom-ise I read in His word; Bless-ed are they who have died in the Lord;
Soon shall I be from the wick-ed re-leased, Soon shall the wea-ry for-ev-er be blest,

My heart doth leap while I hear Je-sus say, There, there is rest, there is rest.
I will go for-ward, for this is my theme; There, there is rest, there is rest.
They will be called to re-ceive their re-ward; Then, there is rest, there is rest.
Soon shall I lean up-on Je-sus' breast, Then, there is rest, there is rest.

I LONG TO BE THERE

It is a bit difficult to know whether this hymn should be classed as a Millerite Adventist hymn or a pioneer Sabbathkeeping Adventist hymn. It did not appear in either the 1842 or 1843 edition of the *Millennial Harp*. However, Joshua V. Himes included it in his *Advent Harp*, published in 1849 for Sundaykeeping Adventists. When James White brought out his second hymnal, *Hymns for Second Advent Believers*, in 1852, he also included five of Himes's eight original stanzas, Nos. 1, 3, 4, 7, and 8, in his hymnal.

The hymn continued to be published in all the major Sabbathkeeping Adventist hymnals through the 1876 *Spiritual Songs*.

Whether the hymn was actually sung by the Millerites during their movement is unknown. However, it is one of three hymns that William Miller is said to have enjoyed having sung to him during the illness that preceded his death on December 20, 1849.

It may be that the hymn was most meaningful to those disappointed Adventists who actually experienced the disappointment of October 22, 1844. The taunts and ridicule that they faced during the days and weeks immediately following the Disappointment are hard now to imagine. Joseph Bates later recalled, "The effect of this disappointment can be realized only by those who experienced it."

In his autobiographical memoirs, Hiram Edson wrote, "Our fondest hopes and expectations were blasted, and such a spirit of weeping came over us as I never experienced before. It seemed that the loss of all earthly friends could have been no comparison. We wept and wept, till the day dawn" (quoted in Francis D. Nichol, *The Midnight Cry*, pp. 263, 264).

In 1868, as James White thought back on the day, he recalled in *Life Incidents*, page 182: "True believers had given up all for Christ, and had shared His presence as never before. . . . The love of Jesus filled every soul . . . , and with inexpressible desire they prayed, 'Come Lord Jesus, and come quickly,' but He did not come. And now, to turn again to the cares, perplexities, and dangers of life in full view of the jeers and revilings of unbelievers who now scoffed as never before was a terrible trial of faith and patience.

"When Elder Himes visited Portland, Maine, a few days after the passing of the time, and stated that the brethren should prepare for another cold winter, my feelings were almost uncontrollable. I left the place of the meeting and wept like a child."

In a letter dated December 13, 1844, William Miller wrote: "It passed. And the next day it seemed as though all the demons from the bottomless pit were let loose upon us. The same ones and many more who were crying for mercy two days before, were now mixed with the rabble and mocking, scoffing, and threatening in a most blasphemous manner" (letter printed in Nichol, p. 266).

To suffer the hurt of going through the Disappointment was bad enough, but having to endure the added jeers and ridicule of scoffers made it almost unbearable. Those disappointed Millerites were positive they were in an alien, hostile world. Try as they might, they had no good answer to the question "Why didn't you go up?" Responses such as "And if I had gone up, where would you have gone?" might momentarily silence a critic, but did not really answer the question. It would be some time before further Bible study helped them understand what had gone wrong.

In the months surrounding the Disappointment, further humiliation was heaped upon a number of Millerites as they were put under legal guardianship by relatives and others who claimed that such was necessary to protect the assets of the "deceived." Adding the belief that the seventh day is the Sabbath did nothing to help convince skeptical relatives that our pioneers were sane. Those definitely were not easy times.

Persecution and troubles continued for several years. As late as 1859 a man wrote to the *Review and Herald* from Ohio, telling how critics were discussing Adventist doctrines freely "and often angrily." Another wrote to tell how an opposing minister mimicked and satirized him. There was also a report about a prayer meeting in Pennsylvania being disrupted by a shower of stones and the shooting off of firearms near the door. Two French-speaking ministers were warned to move on or be tarred and feathered. Even though such occurrences did not happen to every Adventist, they happened often enough to magnify Adventists' sense of alienation.

It is easy, therefore, to understand why the early Adventists sang this hymn that begins "In the midst of temptation and sorrow, and strife." "I Long to Be There" was not just a cliché, but expressed their heartfelt desire.

I Long to Be There

From Advent Harp, *1849*

From Advent Harp, *1849*

Arr. by Sandra G. Gray, 1988

1. In the midst of temp-ta - tion, and sor - row and strife, And
2. When pov - er - ty press - es, and foes do sur-round, And
3. When this mor-tal bod - y is rack - ing with pain, And
4. When the wick - ed are scoff - ing, be - cause I be-lieve The

ev - ils un - num - bered, of this bit - ter life, I
clouds of thick dark - ness do hov - ver a - round The
de - mons are striv - ing to trou - ble my brain, I
Sav - ior is com - ing, my pains to re - lieve, I

look to a bless'd earth, free from all care, The
path - way to glo - ry which Christ did pre - pare, I
hope for the crown that the saints soon shall wear, In the
weep for their fol - ly, and bow in deep pray'r, For

king - dom of Je - sus, and
look for His com - ing, and long to be there,
re - gions of glo - ry, and long to be there,
Christ's com - ing king - dom, and

The king - dom of Je - sus,
long   to   be   there,   I   look   for   His   com - ing,   and   long   to   be   there!
In the re - gions of glo - ry,
For Christ's com-ing king -dom,

5. And when cruel death with his spear lifted high,
      Stands full in my presence, and says, thou shalt die!
   I think how my Savior its smart once did bear,
      To fit me for Eden, and long to be there!

6. When the grave, with its millions of captives, appears
      To the eye of my mind, it awakens my fear:
   I yearn for that morn, when the dead saints shall wear
      Their glorified bodies, and long to be there!

7. By the sweet flowing River of Life I will sing
      My triumph through Jesus, my Savior and King,
   And praise Him who brought me, a sinner, to share
      A feast of fat things, O, I long to be there!

8. I long to be there! and the thought that 'tis near
      Makes me almost impatient for Christ to appear,
   And fit up that dwelling of glories so rare,
      The earth robed in beauty, I long to be there!

I'M A PILGRIM

everal of the hymns that were sung by the Millerite Adventists spoke of the feelings of alienation that they felt toward this world as they looked forward to meeting their soon-returning Lord. "I'm a Pilgrim" is an example of that type of song. After the disappointment of October 22, 1844, this hymn continued to express the feelings of isolation that early Sabbathkeepers also felt.

Joseph Bates, a retired sea captain who had become a Millerite preacher, recounted an incident regarding this particular hymn in his *Autobiography*, published in 1868. It happened when he and Heman S. Gurney, known as the "singing blacksmith," took a trip through Maryland in February and early March of 1844 to hold evangelistic meetings. (See "Lo! An Angel Loud Proclaiming" for additional information about H. S. Gurney.) At one of their evening meetings, several slaves came to hear the singing and preaching.

As Bates recalled: "[The slaves at the meeting] seemed delighted with the Advent hymns. They heard Brother Gurney sing the hymn 'I'm a Pilgrim and I'm a Stranger.' One of the Colored men came to our lodgings to beg one of the printed copies. Brother Gurney had but one. Said he, 'I'll give you a quarter of a dollar for it.' Probably it was all the money the poor fellow had. He lingered as though he could not be denied. Brother Gurney then copied it for him, which pleased him very much" (p. 284).

The hymn "I'm a Pilgrim" appeared in both the 36-page and later the 72-page *Supplement* to the 1843 edition of the *Millennial Harp*, published by Joshua V. Himes for use by the Millerites. James White included the hymn in his 1849 hymnbook entitled *Hymns for God's Peculiar People That Keep the Commandments of God and the Faith of Jesus*. It has continued to be retained in Seventh-day Adventist hymnals to the present.

I'm a Pilgrim

Mary S. B. Dana, 1841 (1810-1883)

Arr. from an Italian air

1. I'm a pil-grim, and I'm a stran-ger; I can tar-ry, I can
2. There the glo-ry is ev-er shin-ing! O, my long-ing heart, my
3. There's the cit-y to which I jour-ney; My Re-deem-er, my Re-
4. Fare-well, drear-y earth, by sin so blight-ed, In im-mor-tal beau-ty

tar-ry but a night; Do not de-tain me, for I am go-ing
long-ing heart is there; Here in this coun-try so dark and drear-y,
deem-er is its light! There is no sor-row, nor an-y sigh-ing,
soon you'll be ar-rayed! He who has formed thee will soon re-store thee!

To where the foun-tains are ev-er flow-ing.
I long have wan-dered for-lorn and wea-ry.
Nor an-y tears there, or an-y dy-ing.
And then Thy dread curse shall nev-er more be:

I'm a pil-grim,

and I'm a stran-ger; I can tar-ry, I can tar-ry but a night.

JERUSALEM

In 1841 Joshua V. Himes and Josiah Litch compiled *Millennial Musings*, the first Millerite hymnal. It contained no music, only words. Among the hymns they included was "Jerusalem." As printed originally, it had only the stanzas, no chorus. When Himes reprinted the hymn in the 1843 *Millennial Harp*, this time it was set to music, and the chorus was included. Today's Adventists are familiar with the tune Himes chose because it is the same tune we still use when singing "Never Part Again." Interestingly, "Never Part Again" is not found in any Millerite hymnals, but as noted, "Jerusalem" is included—both with and without the ever-popular chorus.

The hymn, including the chorus, was later reprinted by James White in *Hymns for Second Advent Believers*. It continued to be reprinted, though without chorus or music, in hymnals until *Hymns and Tunes* appeared in 1886. The first time that music is given for the version without the chorus is in *Hymns and Tunes*. As might be expected, it is a different tune from the one used by the Millerites in their *Millennial Harp* and, presumably, different from the one that James White intended to be used when he published the words and chorus in his 1852 hymnal. From *Hymns and Tunes* through the 1941 *Church Hymnal*, the verses to "Jerusalem" were set to the tune ST. PETER. The 1985 *Seventh-day Adventist Hymnal* still includes only the verses, but the tune there chosen is LAND OF REST.

The 1843 *Millennial Harp* contained two additional stanzas that James White did not reprint in 1852, apparently because he did not agree with some of the theology they contained. White completely rewrote stanza 4 and just eliminated the original stanza 5, so the hymn as he reprinted it contained a total of five stanzas rather than the six used in the 1843 *Millennial Harp*.

The two original stanzas that James White did not use are:

> 4. If heaven be thus glorious, Lord,
> > Why should I stay from hence.
> > What folly's this that I should dread
> > To die, and go from hence.

5. Reach down, O Lord, Thine arm of grace,
   And cause me to ascend,
   Where congregations ne'er break up,
   And Sabbaths never end.

The 1843 *Millennial Harp* ended with a sixth stanza. James White used the same last stanza. We are familiar with it because it is also sung as the last stanza of "Amazing Grace." The five stanzas included in *Early Advent Singing* are the same as those used by James White in his 1852 hymnal.

Neither the author's identity nor that of the tune writer is known for certain.

There is a subtle but interesting difference between the chorus of "Never Part Again" as it is printed in the 1985 *Seventh-day Adventist Hymnal* and the chorus of "Jerusalem" as printed in the 1843 *Millennial Harp* and as originally sung by the Millerites.

1985—"And *soon* we shall *with Jesus reign* . . ."
1843—"And *then* we shall *our Jesus meet* . . ."

While doubtless the Millerites looked forward to "reigning" with Christ, what really excited William Miller and his followers was "meeting" Jesus. Miller was a man who had thoroughly fallen in love with Jesus. He wrote, "They [the Scriptures] became my delight, and in Jesus I found a friend."

In 1834 Miller exclaimed in a letter to an acquaintance, "Give me Jesus, and a knowledge of His Word, faith in His name, hope in His grace, interest in His love, and let me be clothed in His righteousness, and the world may enjoy all the high-sounding titles, the riches it can boast, the vanities it is heir to, and all the pleasures of sin; and they will be no more to me than a drop in the ocean. Yes, let me have Jesus Christ, and then vanish all earthly toys. What glory has God revealed in the face of Jesus Christ! In Him all power centers. In Him all power dwells. He is the evidence of all truth, the foundation of all mercy, the giver of all grace, the object of all adoration, and the source of all light; and I hope to enjoy Him to all eternity. What! Such a sinful wretch as I enjoy Christ? How can this be? Yes, yes; through the electing love of God, the sprinkling of the blood of the covenant, and the work of regeneration, such a sinner as I may be cleansed from sin, purified, and made white, and glorified in the New Jerusalem, together with Him, and with all who love our Lord and Saviour Jesus Christ, and who love His appearing"

(Sylvester Bliss, *Memoirs of William Miller*, p. 111).

The thought that even one person might not have the opportunity to choose whether to be saved drove Miller to go preach. He said, "When I was about my business it was continually ringing in my ears, 'Go and tell the world of their danger'" (*William Miller's Apology and Defence*, p. 15). And so he did, year after year, usually giving two two-hour lectures on the prophecies per day. Miller estimated that between 1832 and 1844 he preached 4,500 sermons to at least half a million people.

Although Miller died in 1849 without seeing his fondest hopes realized, Ellen White was shown God's eventual reward for this dedicated pioneer: "Angels watch the precious dust of this servant of God, and he will come forth at the sound of the last trump" (*Early Writings*, p. 258). Finally, on the great resurrection day Miller will get his heart's desire: to meet and be with his friend Jesus.

Jerusalem

Anon, c.1585

From Timbrel of Zion, *1853*
Arr. by Donald F. Haynes (1907-1975)

1. Je - ru - sa-lem, my hap - py home, Oh, how I long for thee!
2. Thy walls are all of prec-ious stone, Most glo - rious to be - hold;
3. Thy gar-den and thy pleas-ant walks My stud - y long have been;
4. Lord, help us by Thy might -y grace To keep in view the prize,
5. When we've been there ten thou-sand years, Bright shin -ing as the sun,

When will my sor - rows have an end, Thy joys when shall I see?
Thy gates are rich - ly set with pearl Thy streets are paved with gold.
Such daz-zling views by hu - man sight Have nev - er yet been seen.
Till Thou dost come to take us home To that blest par - a - dise.
We've no less days to sing God's praise Than when we first be - gun.

Refrain

We're march-ing thro' Im - man-uel's ground, We soon shall hear the

trum - pet sound, And then we shall our Je - sus meet, And

nev - er, nev-er part a - gain. What? nev er part a - gain? No,

nev - er part a - gain. What? nev-er part a -gain? No, nev - er part a -

gain, But there we shall our Je-sus meet, And nev-er, never part a - gain.

LO, WHAT A GLORIOUS SIGHT APPEARS

T he thought of Christ's return has excited Christians ever since He went back to heaven at the end of His sojourn on earth. This hymn speaks about that joyful expectation of Christ's second coming and then of meeting together on "Canaan's happy shore" where "we meet to part no more!"

As a young girl Ellen Harmon (later White) and her family were all members of the Methodist Church. However, after William Miller spoke in Portland, Maine, where the Harmons were living, the Whites became Adventists. In 1843 the Methodists disfellowshipped the Harmon family for being out of harmony with the church.

Years later Ellen White recalled one of the meetings she and her older brother, Robert, attended prior to their finally being disfellowshipped.

"One evening my brother Robert and myself went to class meeting. The [Methodist] presiding elder was present. When it came my brother's turn, he spoke with great humility, yet with clearness, of the necessity for a complete fitness to meet our Saviour when He should come in the clouds of heaven with power and great glory. . . . When I was called upon to speak, I arose. . . . I told the story of my great suffering under the conviction of sin, how I had at length received the blessing so long sought, an entire conformity to the will of God, and expressed my joy in the tidings of the soon coming of my Redeemer to take His children home.

"In my simplicity I expected that my Methodist brethren and sisters would understand my feelings and rejoice with me. But I was disappointed; several sisters groaned and moved their chairs noisily turning their backs upon me. I could not think what had been said to offend them, and spoke very briefly, feeling the chilling influence of their disapprobation. When I had ceased speaking, Elder B. [Charles Baker] asked me if it would not be more pleasant to live a long life of usefulness, doing others good, than to have Jesus come speedily and destroy poor sinners. I replied that I longed for the coming of Jesus. . . .

"He then inquired if I would not rather die peacefully upon my bed than to pass through the pain of being changed, while living, from mortality to immortality. My answer was . . . that I was willing to live or die as God willed, and could easily endure all the pain that could be borne in a moment, in the twinkling of an eye; that I desired the wheels of time to roll swiftly round, and bring the welcome day when these vile bodies should be changed, and fashioned like unto Christ's most glorious body. I also stated that when I lived nearest to the Lord, then I most earnestly longed for His appearing. Here some present seemed to be greatly displeased" (*Testimonies*, vol. 1, pp. 35, 36).

When young Ellen expressed her desire for "the wheels of time to roll swiftly round," she was paraphrasing a line that is repeated twice in the fifth stanza of this hymn: "Fly swifter round, ye wheels of time!" It was a common practice for people in that time to either quote or at least allude to hymns that were meaningful to them when writing to others about their Christian experience.

Nearly 30 years later, James White quoted the same lines about the "wheels of time" in *Bible Adventism*, a printed collection of 10 of his sermons.

The Millerite Adventists included this hymn, written by Isaac Watts about 1707, as the very first hymn in their 1841 *Millennial Musings*, compiled by Joshua V. Himes and Josiah Litch. The hymn was also included the following year in Himes's 1842 *Millennial Harp*.

The hymn's enduring popularity with the Millerites is evidenced by the fact that Himes also included it in his small throwaway-type hymnal called *Second Advent Hymns; Designed to Be Used in Prayer and Camp-Meetings*, which was printed in the same year. The hymn was later printed with the music in the April 6, 1842, issue of the *Signs of the Times*, as well as in the January 27, 1843, issue of *The Midnight Cry*, both Millerite papers. And later that year Himes included it again in the 1843 edition of the *Millennial Harp*.

When James White published his first hymnal in 1849, called *Hymns for God's Peculiar People That Keep the Commandments of God and the Faith of Jesus*, he also included this hymn, though with some variation in the wording. It continued to be published in Seventh-day Adventist hymnals through *Hymns and Tunes*, which first came out in 1886. The hymn is once again included in the 1985 *Seventh-day Adventist Hymnal*. The tune used in the present hymnal is the same one used by the Millerites. So this hymn has remained virtually unchanged since its introduction among Adventists in the 1840s.

Himes used one stanza in his hymnal that was not later reprinted in Seventh-day Adventist hymnals:

> The God of glory down to men
> Removes His blest abode;
> Men are the objects of His love,
> And He their gracious God.

Lo, What a Glorious Sight Appears

Rev. 21: 1-4   NEW JERUSALEM
Isaac Watts, 1707 (1674-1748)   Attr. to Abraham D. Merrill (1796-1878)

1. Lo, what a glo-rious sight ap-pears To our be-liev - ing eyes! The earth and seas are passed a - way, And the old roll - ing skies. And the old roll - ing skies. The

2. From the third heaven where God re-sides, That ho - ly, hap - py place; The New Je - ru - sa - lem comes down, A-dorn'd with shin - ing grace. A - dorn'd with shin - ing grace. The

3. At - tend - ing an - gels shout for joy And the bright ar - mies sing-- Mor - tals! be - hold the sa - cred seat Of your de-scend - ing King. Of your de-scend - ing King; Mor -

4. His own soft hand shall wipe the tears From ev - ery weep - ing eye; And pains, and groans, and griefs, and fears, And death it - self shall die! And death it - self shal die, And death it - self shall die; And

5. How long, dear Sav - ior! oh, how long Shall this bright hour de - lay? Fly swift - er round, ye wheels of time! And bring the wel - come day. And bring the wel - come day; Fly

35

earth and seas are passed a - way, And the old roll - ing skies.
New Je - ru - sa - lem comes down, A - dorn'd with shin - ing grace.
tals! be-hold the sa - cred seat Of your de-scend -ing King.
pains, and groans, and griefs, and fears, And death it - self shall die.
swift - er round, ye wheels of time! And bring the wel - come day.

Refrain

O that will be joy - ful, joy - ful, joy - ful!

O that will be joy - ful When we meet to part no more! When we

meet to part no more on Ca - naan's hap - py shore; 'Tis

there we'll meet at Je - sus' feet, When we meet to part no more!

36

MY BIBLE LEADS TO GLORY

The Scriptures were central to the thinking and beliefs of the Millerites. William Miller himself spent the years from 1816 to 1818 studying his Bible, with nothing but a concordance to aid him.

Prior to his finding Christ as a personal friend, Miller subscribed to deism, a popular philosophy of his day. Individuals holding that view believed that God created the world but then He took no personal interest in either people or the affairs of nations. It was as if God wound up a clock to get it going and then took off through the universe to do something else, without giving any further attention to the clock.

But a change slowly came into William Miller's thinking. He wrote:

"I saw that the Bible did bring to view just such a Saviour as I needed; and I was perplexed to find how an uninspired book should develop principles so perfectly adapted to the wants of a fallen world. I was constrained to admit that the Scriptures must be a revelation from God. They became my delight; and in Jesus I found a friend. The Saviour became to me the chiefest among ten thousand; and the Scriptures, which before were dark and contradictory, now became the lamp to my feet and the light to my path. My mind became settled and satisfied. I found the Lord God to be a Rock in the midst of the ocean of life. The Bible now became my chief study, and I can truly say, I searched it with great delight. I found the half was never told me. I wondered why I had not seen its beauty and glory before, and marveled that I could have ever rejected it. I found everything revealed that my heart could desire, and a remedy for every disease of the soul. I lost all taste for other reading, and applied my heart to get wisdom from God" (Bliss, *Memoirs of William Miller*, p. 67).

During the years 1816 to 1818, Miller read no commentaries because he did not want to be confused by various teachings that they might contain. Rather, he started reading Genesis, and read right through his Bible. When he came across a word that he did not understand, he looked it up in his concordance to see how the word was used elsewhere in the Bible. Thus the Bible itself became its own interpreter for him. By 1818, when he had completed his initial study, not only had he found a personal Saviour, but he had also discovered the 2300-day prophecy of Daniel 8:14.

From 1818 to 1823 William Miller continued to study his Bible in an attempt to discover if there was an error regarding the time prophecy. He could find nothing at all in Scripture that would disprove his understanding that the prophecy would end about the year 1843. In fact the more he studied, the more it seemed to him that his understanding was correct. Years later Miller recalled that during those five years he thought of every argument that was later used against him by his critics, and in every instance he found a Bible answer that satisfied him.

Since Miller is now associated with the date October 22, 1844, as the time for Christ's return, one cannot help wondering why he never read Matthew 24:36: "But of that day and hour knoweth no man, no, not the angels of heaven, but my Father only." The fact is, Miller knew that text very well, and that is why he never set a precise date. He felt that Christ would return sometime between March 21, 1843, and March 21, 1844.

It was Samuel S. Snow who began proclaiming the October 22 date. William Miller himself did not accept the date until October 6, just over two weeks before it arrived. However, he finally concluded that God's Spirit was so evident in what was called the "seventh-month movement" that the October 22 date must be correct. In a letter to Joshua V. Himes, Miller exclaimed, "I see a glory in the seventh month which I never saw before. . . . I am almost home, Glory! Glory!! Glory!!!"

Of course, the date is correct—it was the interpretation as to the event that was wrong. Rather than pointing to Christ's return as happening on that day, the prophecy pointed toward the beginning of the cleansing of the heavenly sanctuary. But Miller never came to understand that. He was old and worn out, and it was others who discovered what actually happened on October 22.

As much as Miller wanted to see his best friend, Jesus, he was concerned that once again he and his followers would be disappointed. On the evening of October 21, the night before they believed Jesus would return, Miller told the expectant Adventists gathered at his house about his reservations. And what were Miller's fears based on? Why, the Bible of course. Jesus' coming is predicted in Luke 12:40 as occurring when least expected. And as Miller surely must have pointed out to his friends that evening, the next day they all would be on the lookout for Christ. There was absolutely no way

He could arrive unexpectedly.

This hymn was included by Joshua V. Himes in his small throwaway-type hymnal published in 1842 called *Second Advent Hymns; Designed to Be Used in Prayer and Camp-Meetings*. It was reprinted in the 1843 edition of the *Millennial Harp*. The hymn was not picked up by James White in any of his hymnals for Sabbathkeepers, though Himes included it in his 1849 *Advent Harp*, published for Sundaykeeping Adventists.

That James White knew and sang this hymn before the Disappointment is confirmed in an editorial he wrote in the December 1849 issue of *Present Truth*. Speaking about the biblical basis that undergirds Adventist belief in the prophecies, he commented, "When we in 1843 sang, 'My Bible Leads to Glory,' we sang a true statement. It did not stop in 1844, and 'lead' us around another way, no, no. . . . Glory to God," he exclaimed, " 'My Bible leads to glory.' Amen."

My Bible Leads to Glory

From Millenial Harp, *1843*
From Second Advent Hymns, *1842*
Arr. by Sandra G. Gray, 1988

1. My Bi - ble leads to glo - ry, My Bi - ble leads to glo - ry, My
2. Re - li - gion makes me hap - py, Re - li - gion makes me hap - py, Re -
3. I'm on my way to glo - ry, I'm on my way to glo - ry, I'm

Bi - ble leads to glo - ry,
li - gion makes me hap - py, Ye fol - low-ers of the Lamb.
on my way to glo - ry,

Refrain

Sing on, pray on, ye fol - low-ers of Im - man - u - el,

Sing on, pray on, ye fol - low-ers of the Lamb.

4. I'm fighting for a kingdom,
5. King Jesus is my captain,
6. We'll have a shout in glory,
7. There we shall live forever,

40

MY BROTHER, I WISH YOU WELL

William Miller preached his warning message of Christ's soon return from August 1831 until the disappointment of October 22, 1844. During his lifetime he was known as a man of compassion and genuine concern for others. It is reported that on occasion as he was speaking he might notice an elderly man or woman looking over the congregation trying to locate a vacant place to sit. From his vantage point in the pulpit, Miller could see the empty seats. He would stop his preaching, leave the platform, and help the person find a seat. Then he would return to the pulpit and continue with his sermon. Even the critics of his message could not argue with that kind of religion!

In 1839 William Miller received an invitation from Timothy Cole, pastor of a church in Lowell, Massachusetts, to speak to his congregation. Cole arranged to meet Miller at the train station. Having never met Miller (he knew him only by reputation as the famous revivalist preacher), Cole assumed that his guest was a handsome man of commanding appearance. As the passengers alighted from the train and departed the station, only one man, stocky in appearance and shaking slightly from palsy, remained. He was wearing a camlet coat and a white hat.

Cole was afraid even to think that this could possibly be William Miller. When learning that he was, Cole was highly embarrassed that he had invited such a person to speak at his church. Cole led Miller home, where they ate their dinner in almost total silence.

As the time for the meeting approached, Cole took Miller to his church, only to discover, much to his chagrin, that the place was nearly packed. After introducing William Miller to the eagerly awaiting congregation, Cole refused to remain seated on the platform with him. Instead, he walked down and sat in the audience with the others.

Apparently not noticing this slight, William Miller started right in. He read a hymn and asked the people to join in singing it. Then after having them sing a second hymn, he began speaking. Miller chose as his text, "Looking for that blessed hope, and the glorious appearing of the great God and our Saviour Jesus Christ" (Titus 2:13). Within 15 minutes, Timothy Cole was so moved by what he was hearing that he got up out of his seat, walked back up on the platform, and sat there throughout the remainder of the sermon. Cole then asked Miller to stay on to hold more meetings in his church. At their conclusion, Timothy Cole himself became a Millerite preacher.

We are reminded that when it comes to inviting others to Christ, one does not have to be physically handsome or beautiful to be successful. Rather, God needs those who are totally dedicated to Him. Beauty of character is of more importance than beauty of face. Ellen White once wrote: "The worker for God should put forth the highest mental and moral energies with which nature, cultivation, and the grace of God have endowed him; but his success will be proportionate to the degree of consecration and self-sacrifice in which his work is done, rather than to either natural or acquired endowments" (*Counsels to Parents and Teachers*, pp. 537, 538).

The chorus "My Brother, I Wish You Well" was published by Joshua V. Himes in both the 1842 and 1843 editions of his *Millennial Harp*. The chorus was included in the 1886 *Hymns and Tunes* in a section called "Miscellaneous—Old Melodies," the only time it was ever reprinted in a Seventh-day Adventist hymnal. Rather than including separate stanzas for "My Father, . . ." and "My mother, . . ." in *Hymns and Tunes*, these two stanzas were combined into "My parents, . . ." In addition, a fifth stanza, "Poor sinner, I wish you well, . . ." was added, bringing to five the total number of stanzas printed in *Hymns and Tunes*.

The message of this chorus was simple, straightforward, and genuinely felt by the Millerites toward those around them. They were convinced that Jesus would soon return, and they did all within their power to warn others of that fact.

My Brother, I Wish You Well

From Millenial Harp, *1842*   *Arr. from* Millenial Harp, *1842*

1. My broth-er I wish you well, My broth-er I wish you well,
2. My sis-ter I wish you well, My sis-ter I wish you well,
3. My fath-er I wish you well, My fath-er I wish you well,

When my Lord calls I trust I shall Be men-tioned in the prom-ised land.

Refrain

Be men-tioned in the prom-ised land, Be men-tioned in the prom-ised land,

When my Lord calls I trust I shall Be men-tioned in the pro-mised land.

4. My mother, I wish you well,
5. My neighbors, I wish you well,
6. My pastor, I wish you well,
7. Young converts, I wish you well,
8. Poor sinner, I wish you well,

NEVER PART AGAIN

N ever Part Again" has been a perennial favorite with Adventist congregations ever since the closing days of the Millerite movement in 1844. Since at least 1922 it has been sung at most General Conference sessions, and many conferences still use it to close their camp meetings each year.

One account has it that the hymn was also used by Millerites to close their camp meetings and other general meetings. It is easy to understand how, believing that Christ would return on Tuesday, October 22, 1844, at the close of the 2300-day prophecy of Daniel 8:14, they would love this song.

It is almost possible to hear, in one's imagination, the strains of this hymn being fervently sung by those earnest believers. Somewhere in the hills of New England, a camp meeting is closing and each person present wonders, *Will I ever meet my friends on earth again? Or will our next meeting take place in that land of pure delight, where bliss eternal reigns?* The smell of pine needles that have been strewn down the aisles between crude wooden benches to help control the dust in the large tent commingles with the smoke from the now-dying fires of the campers.

Slowly the entire group assembles in a large circle—almost hesitatingly it seems, as if they are in no rush to get back home to the scorn and ridicule of their former friends and associates. With tears of expectant joy they begin to sing, softly at first, and then louder, as they move toward the end of the hymn. At last they are through and the echo of the music fades away. Gradually the campers drift back to their tents to pack their goods and head home. In just a little time, they fervently believe, Jesus will return.

But He did not come as expected, and many thousands were crushed with disappointment. What about William Miller himself? He never understood what went wrong. But one thing Miller knew—Jesus had promised He would return. And he was also convinced that the day was not far off. Miller later wrote, "I have fixed my mind upon another time. . . . And that is *Today*, TODAY, and *TODAY*, until He comes."

This old hymn, originally written by Isaac Watts in the early 1700s, continued to be one of William Miller's favorites. Shortly before his death on December 20, 1849, it is reported that he repeated the words of these verses over and over. And it was one of three hymns that he asked the members of his family to sing to him again and again.

Although Isaac Watts' original stanzas were sung by the Millerites, there apparently is no evidence that they were sung to the tune we currently use, or that the chorus as we now sing it was included with the stanzas when sung by the Millerites. Interestingly, no Millerite hymnal even included the stanzas. The first Seventh-day Adventist hymnal to include the stanzas, though in modified form, was the 1876 *Spiritual Songs*. The tune used was VARINA. This same combination of stanzas and hymn tune continued to be used in Seventh-day Adventist hymnals through the 1941 *Church Hymnal*. The original tune used by the Millerites for the stanzas is not known for certain.

As popular as "Never Part Again" in its present form has become with Seventh-day Adventist audiences, it was not until the 1985 *Seventh-day Adventist Hymnal* that it was published in just that form in a major denominational hymnbook. It had been included in *Gospel Melodies and Evangelistic Hymns*, 1944, and it was also printed separately as sheet music.

Never Part Again

From Timbrel of Zion, 1853
Arr. by Donald F. Haynes (1907-1975)

Isaac Watts (1674-1748)

1. There is a land of pure de-light, Where bliss e - ter - nal reigns,
2. There ev - er-last -ing spring a-bides, And nev - er with-'ring flowers,
3. Could we but stand where Mos-es stood, And view the land-scape o'er,

In - fi - nite day ex - cludes the night And plea - sures ban -ish pain.
And but a lit - tle space di-vides This heav - 'nly land from ours.
Not all this world's pre - tend - ed good Could ev - er charm us more.

Refrain

We're trav-'ling to Im - man-uel's land, We soon shall hear the trum-pet sound,

And soon we shall with Je - sus reign, And nev-er, nev-er part a - gain.

46

What!   Nev -er part a - gain? No,   nev - er part a - gain, What!

Nev-er part   a -gain? No,   nev - er part   a - gain, And   soon we

shall with   Je - sus reign, And   nev -er, nev-er part a - gain.

ONE PRECIOUS BOON,
O LORD, I SEEK

Among the prominent Millerite leaders, Charles Fitch (1805-1844) was the only one who actually wrote a hymn. Prior to his joining the movement, Charles Fitch was a Presbyterian minister who pastored the important Marlboro Chapel in Boston and had written a pamphlet against slavery. In 1838 Fitch was given a copy of William Miller's book on the prophecies. After reading it, he wrote to Miller expressing his interest in Miller's views and stating that he felt Miller's position was correct. Fitch told Miller that he planned to present Miller's views at the next ministerial association meeting.

Although Fitch's presentation caused a sensation at the meeting, it was not the reaction he had hoped for. His ministerial associates treated his views on the prophecies with such ridicule and contempt that for a while he gave them up and went back to his previous beliefs. But his mind was not at rest. Because of William Miller's need for a large enough hall to accommodate the crowds, in 1839 Fitch arranged for Miller to hold his second series of lectures in Boston in Fitch's Marlboro Chapel.

By 1841 Fitch had left his Boston church and, after pastoring in New Jersey for a time, had moved on to lead a church in Haverhill, Massachusetts. Another minister, Josiah Litch, of Philadelphia, helped Charles Fitch once again to accept the subject of the Second Coming. Some of Fitch's former friends turned against him, but others, including Dr. W. C. Palmer and his wife, Phoebe, accepted the Advent message. Phoebe Palmer wrote many hymns, including "Watch, Ye Saints."

In 1842 Charles Fitch and Apollos Hale, one of his parishioners at the Haverhill Winter Street church, designed the famous "1843" prophetic chart. They painted a sample on cloth and took it to the Boston General Conference of May 1842, over which Joseph Bates presided as chairman. The reaction was so positive that the conference voted to have 300 copies printed and made available for use.

Charles Fitch is described as a cogent reasoner and powerful preacher. Late in 1842 he moved to Cleveland, Ohio, where he continued to proclaim the Advent message. He held a series of meetings at Oberlin College in 1842, a second series the following year, and yet another series in Cleveland. As Fitch made a call for the penitent to come forward for special prayer, a "big lumbering" fellow started with others down the stairway to respond. He stumbled and fell. The crowd began to laugh. Fitch quelled their laughter by saying, "Never mind, brother; it is better to stumble into heaven than to walk straight into hell."

Fitch was the first to urge people to leave their various churches and to "come out of Babylon." In the summer of 1843 he printed a sermon to this effect in the paper he had published. His contention was that by rejecting the Advent message the Protestant churches had become the Babylon out of which people are called by the second angel mentioned in Revelation 14.

After all his energetic efforts to prepare people to meet the Lord, Fitch did not live until October 22, 1844. (The story of his death, which occurred on October 14, 1844, is told under the hymn "Watch Ye Saints.")

Charles Fitch is said to have written his hymn, "One Precious Boon, O Lord, I Seek," after accepting the Advent message, when most of his friends turned against him.

The tune used for this hymn is UXBRIDGE. It was composed in 1830 by Lowell Mason (1792-1872). Fitch's hymn itself was not printed in either the 1842 or 1843 edition of the *Millennial Harp*, and Joshua V. Himes did not include it in his 1849 *Advent Harp* for Sundaykeeping Adventists. James White first included it in his second hymnal, published in 1852, called *Hymns for Second Advent Believers*. It was last printed in the 1941 *Church Hymnal*.

One Precious Boon, O Lord, I Seek

UXBRIDGE

Charles Fitch (1805-1844)

Lowell Mason, 1830 (1830-1872)

1. One pre-cious boon, O Lord, I seek, While tossed up-on life's
2. Earth's scoffs and scorn well-pleased I'll bear, Nor mourn tho' un-der-
3. The friends I love may turn from me, Their words un-kind may
4. Let me but know, where-e'er I roam, That I am do-ing
5. To that bright, blest, im-mor-tal morn, By ho-ly pro-phets
6. Then all the scoffs and scorn I've borne For His dear sake who

bil - low-y sea; To hear a voice with-in me speak,
foot I'm trod, If day by day I may but share
pierce me through; But this my dai-ly prayer shall be,
Je - sus' will; And though I've nei-ther friends nor home.
long fore - told, My ea - ger, long-ing eyes I turn,
died for me, To ev-er-last-ing joys will turn,

"Thy Sav - ior is well - pleased with thee."
Thine ap - pro - ba - tion, O my God!
"For - give; they know not what they do."
My heart shall glow with glad - ness still.
And soon its glo - ries shall be - hold.
In glo - rious im - mor - tal - i - ty.

50

PRAYER OF THE CHURCH

This hymn was included by Joshua V. Himes in his small throwaway-type hymnal that he published in 1842 and called *Second Advent Hymns; Designed to Be Used in Prayer and Camp-Meetings*. There the hymn is titled "How Long, O Lord?" It was also printed under that title as a poem, without music, in the November 21, 1842, issue of the Millerite paper, *The Midnight Cry*. It was reprinted with music in the February 3, 1843, issue of the same paper. The hymn was included in the 1843 edition of the *Millennial Harp* under the title "Prayer of the Church."

The tune, written in 1837 by George James Webb (1803-1887), was originally for a secular song that began "'Tis dawn, the lark is singing."

The words of the hymn "Prayer of the Church" accurately portray the feelings of those Millerite Adventists who were eagerly awaiting the return of the Lord. Especially as they approached the termination year of the 2300-day prophecy of Daniel 8:14, which they mistakenly thought would usher in the second coming of Christ, did they ask the question "How long, O Lord?"

William Miller himself never set a precise day for Christ's return. He thought it would be sometime between March 21, 1843, and March 21, 1844. Since he had not fixed upon a precise date, the Millerites wondered each day during that seemingly endless year how many more days they would have to live on this earth before Christ's second coming.

Shortly after the first disappointment, in the spring of 1844, William Miller wrote the following lines:

> How tedious and lonesome the hours,
>   While Jesus, my Saviour, delays!
> I have sought Him in solitude's bowers,
>   And looked for Him all the long days.

> Yet He lingers—I pray tell why
>   His chariot no sooner returns?
> To see Him in clouds of the sky,
>   My soul with intensity burns.

51

I long to be with Him at home,
   My heart swallowed up in His love,
On the fields of New Eden to roam,
   And to dwell with my Saviour above.

In the 1843 edition of the *Millennial Harp*, another hymn called "Hymn for 1843" followed "Prayer of the Church." It was designed to be sung to the same tune. Joshua V. Himes had earlier published this second hymn in his small throwaway-type evangelistic hymnal under the title "Your Great Deliverer's Nigh." The words only were printed in the June 29, 1842, issue of *Signs of the Times*, a Millerite paper. The author was given as "Dr. West." No doubt the graphic language of the words and their application to the situation the Millerites found themselves in as they approached what they thought would be the last year of the earth's existence are the reasons the title was changed to "Hymn for 1843."

In 1849 Himes published another hymnal, called the *Advent Harp*. Both of these hymns are printed in it. The first one was still called "Prayer of the Church," but the second was now entitled "The Conflagration." James White never printed "Hymn for 1843," but he reprinted "Prayer of the Church," starting with his 1855 hymnal. The hymn was also printed in the 1908 edition of *Christ in Song*, where it was entitled "How Long?" The tune has always remained unchanged, but for some reason Himes's original third stanza has been deleted whenever the hymn has been reprinted in Seventh-day Adventist hymnals.

Prayer of the Church

WEBB

From Second Advent Hymnal, *1842*   *George James Webb, 1837 (1803-1887)*

1. How long, O Lord our Sav - ior, Wilt Thou re - main a - way?
2. How long, O gra-cious Mas - ter, Wilt Thou Thy house-hold leave?
3. How long, O heav-'nly Bride-groom, How long wilt Thou de - lay?
4. O wake Thy slumb'ring vir - gins; Send forth the so - lemn cry.

Our hearts are grow-ing wea - ry Of Thy so long de - lay.
So long hast Thou now tar - ried, Few Thy re - turn be - lieve.
And yet how few are griev - ing That Thou dost ab - sent stay!
Let all Thy saints re - peat it, "The Bride-groom draw-eth nigh!"

O when shall come the mo - ment When, bright - er far than morn,
Im - mersed in sloth and fol - ly, Thy ser-vants Lord we see;
Thy ver - y Bride her por - tion And call - ing hath for - got,
May all our lamps be burn - ing, Our loins well - gird - ed be,

The sun -shine of Thy glo - ry Shall on Thy peo - ple dawn?
And few of us stand read - y With joy to wel - come Thee.
And seeks for ease and glo - y Where Thou, her Lord, art not.
Each long - ing heart pre - par - ing With joy Thy face to see.

53

THE MERCY SEAT

One distinctive belief of the emerging group of Sabbathkeepers after the Great Disappointment was the sanctuary doctrine. Even though James White included no songs on that topic in his 1849 hymnal, he did put this hymn in his second hymnal, published in 1852 and entitled *Hymns for Second Advent Believers*.

In 1818, when William Miller discovered the Daniel 8:14 text, "Unto two thousand and three hundred days; then shall the sanctuary be cleansed," he erroneously concluded that it referred to the second coming of Christ. Miller set the date for that to happen sometime between the spring of 1843 and the spring of 1844. Later the chronology was changed by Samuel S. Snow to the date October 22, 1844. The new view also included an expanded understanding of the sanctuary types and symbols.

On the morning of October 23, 1844, the day after the Great Disappointment, Adventist pioneer Hiram Edson became the first to understand the explanation for the disappointment the previous day: "Instead of our High Priest coming out of the Most Holy of the heavenly sanctuary to come to this earth . . . at the end of the 2300 days, that He for the first time entered on that day the second apartment of that sanctuary; and that He had a work to perform in the Most Holy before coming to this earth" (*SDA Encyclopedia* [1976], p. 1280).

It became clear to Edson that the sanctuary to be cleansed was not the earth, as William Miller thought, but rather the heavenly sanctuary, and thus the Second Coming was directly involved in that prophecy. The results of further study on the topic by himself and others were written out by O.R.L. Crosier, one of Hiram Edson's friends. Crosier's article was printed in the *Day-Star Extra* (Cincinnati, Ohio) of February 7, 1846.

Crosier's expansion of Edson's heavenly sanctuary idea became the basis of the standard position of early Sabbathkeepers. In addition, they came to realize that the cleansing of the sanctuary also involved a work of judgment.

Although this hymn was not written by Sabbathkeepers, its theme of the mercy seat in the heavenly sanctuary was one they could certainly identify with. About that mercy seat, Ellen White has written:

"The ark that enshrines the tables of the law is covered with the mercy seat, before which Christ pleads His blood in the sinner's behalf. Thus is represented the union of justice and mercy in the plan of human redemption. . . . It is a union that fills all heaven with wonder and adoration. The cherubim of the earthly sanctuary, looking reverently down upon the mercy seat, represent the interest with which the heavenly host contemplate the work of redemption. This is the mystery of mercy into which angels desire to look—that God can be just while He justifies the repenting sinner and . . . that Christ could stoop to raise unnumbered multitudes from the abyss of ruin and clothe them with the spotless garments of His own righteousness to unite with angels who have never fallen and to dwell forever in the presence of God" (*The Great Controversy*, p. 415).

The hymn "The Mercy Seat" was written by Hugh Stowell (1799-1865), rector of Christ Church, Salford, Lancashire, and canon of Chester in England, who had it published in 1828 under the title "Peace at the Mercy Seat."

The tune RETREAT was composed in 1840 by Thomas Hastings (1784-1872) and was published in 1842 in his *Sacred Songs*. Joshua V. Himes included the hymn in his 1843 edition of the *Millennial Harp* for use by Millerite Adventists. The words as found in the 1985 *Seventh-day Adventist Hymnal*, No. 527, are slightly altered from the way both Joshua V. Himes and James White originally printed them. When first printed, the hymn included six stanzas. When *Hymns and Tunes* was published in 1886, the words of the fourth stanza were altered, and the sixth stanza was dropped. All six stanzas, as originally printed by Himes in 1843 and White in 1852, are included here.

The Mercy Seat

Ex. 25:22
Hugh Stowell, 1828 (1799-1865)

RETREAT
Thomas Hastings, 1842 (1784-1872)

1. From ev - ery storm - y wind that blows, From ev - ery swell - ing
2. There is a place where Je - sus sheds The oil of glad - ness
3. There is a scene where spir - its blend, Where friend holds fel - low-
4. Ah! whith - er should we flee for aid, When temp - ted, des - o
5. There, there, on an - gels wings we soar And sin and sense seem
6. O, let my hand for - get her skill, My tongue be si - lent,

tide of woes, There is a calm, a sure re - treat,
on our heads, A place than all be - sides more sweet,
ship with friend: Though sun - dered far, by faith they meet
late, dis-mayed? Or how the hosts of sin de - feat,
all no more, The Lord comes down our souls to greet,
cold and still; This bound - ing heart for - get to beat

'Tis found be - neath the
It is the blood - bought
A - round one com - mon
Had suf - fering saints no
And glo - ry crowns the
If I for - get the

Mer - cy seat.

56

TOGETHER LET US SWEETLY LIVE

This hymn was published by Joshua V. Himes in both his 1842 and 1843 editions of the *Millennial Harp*, designed for use by Millerite Adventists. The words only were also published in his small throwaway-type hymnal, 1842, entitled *Second Advent Hymns; Designed to Be Used in Prayer and Camp-Meetings*. That smaller hymnal was possibly prepared for use in the large Millerite tent that was constructed that year—the largest tent made in America up to that time.

Both *Millennial Harps* also carried words to another Millerite hymn called "The Pilgrim's Lot" that was to be sung to the same tune as "Together Let Us Sweetly Live."

The "Great Tent," as it was called, was 120 feet in diameter, about 50 feet high in the center, and was reported to seat between 3,000 and 4,000 people. Whenever the Millerites pitched their tent, the novelty of it caused thousands of people to come out to find out what was going on and to hear the preaching. From the time the original order for the tent was placed, it was constructed, pitched, and in use within 30 days. There was no time to lose if Christ was about to return!

Apparently the tent cost $615.34. Newspapers were startled at the speed with which it was moved from place to place by wagon, steamboat, or train. A permanent crew of four men had the responsibility of pitching and striking it.

Some people made wagers that the tent would never be filled, but once meetings began, it was always jammed. Railroads even scheduled special trains to accommodate the crowds. A sudden squall in Rochester, New York, snapped 15 chains and gently settled the Great Tent onto the heads of the people. The local citizens raised cash to repair it on condition that the meetings would be continued.

The first Seventh-day Adventist hymnal to include "Together Let Us Sweetly Live" was the 1886 *Hymns and Tunes*, where it was included in a section called "Miscellaneous—Old Melodies" and titled "Bound for the Land of Canaan." The four stanzas used there are included in *Early Advent Singing*. The stanzas used for the

Millerite version of the hymn were somewhat different. In the *Millennial Harp* the hymn contained five stanzas. The second and third stanzas of the Millerite version that were omitted in the 1886 *Hymns and Tunes* were:

2. If you get there before I do,
    I am bound for the land of Canaan.
Look out for me, I'm coming too,
    I am bound for the land of Canaan.

3. I have some friends before me gone,
    I am bound for the land of Canaan.
And I'm resolved to travel on,
    I am bound for the land of Canaan.

In their places was substituted, in 1886, the second stanza that is used in *Early Advent Singing*. When the hymn was next reprinted in the 1985 *Seventh-day Adventist Hymnal*, the wording from the 1886 *Hymns and Tunes* was retained. The other hymn, "The Pilgrim's Lot," has never been reprinted in any Seventh-day Adventist hymnals.

Together Let Us Sweetly Live CANAAN

From Millenial Harp, *1842*   *Early Advent Hymn*

1. To - geth-er let us sweet-ly live,
2. To - geth-er let us watch and pray; I am bound for the land of Ca - naan.
3. Our songs of praise shall fill the skies;
4. Then come with me, be - lov - ed friend;

To - geth-er love to Je - sus give;
And wait Re-demption's joy - ous day;
While high-er still our joys shall rise; I am bound for the land of Ca - naan.
The joys to come shall nev - er end;

Refrain

O Ca - naan, bright Ca - naan, I am bound for the land of Ca - naan. O

Ca-naan, it is my hap - py home, I am bound for the land of Ca - naan.

WATCH, YE SAINTS

The author of this hymn, Mrs. Phoebe Palmer, was a close friend of Millerite leader Charles Fitch. Through Fitch's efforts, both Phoebe and her husband, Dr. W. C. Palmer, became Millerite Adventists. She wrote this particular hymn in 1844. Charles Fitch, along with Apollos Hale, designed the famous "1843" prophetic chart. It depicted in graphic detail the biblical prophecies and symbols used by the Millerites in their preaching. (See "One Precious Boon, O Lord, I Seek" for a hymn written by Charles Fitch.)

With their belief that Christ would soon return, it is natural that hymns on the Second Coming were very popular with the Millerite Adventists. This hymn with its many allusions to Scripture especially appealed to them, since it gave in verse form the signs of the Second Coming. Texts specifically referred to include "the powers of the heavens shall be shaken" (Matt. 24:29); "then all those virgins arose, and trimmed their lamps" (Matt. 25:7); ". . . washed their robes, and made them white in the blood of the Lamb" (Rev. 7:14); "it shall break in pieces and consume all these kingdoms" (Dan. 2:44); "but in the days of the voice of the seventh angel, when he shall begin to sound, the mystery of God shall be finished" (Rev. 10:7); "and then shall they see the Son of man coming in a cloud with power and great glory" (Luke 21:27).

In the weeks just prior to October 22, 1844, Charles Fitch caught cold while baptizing some converts in Lake Erie. He died on Monday, October 14, just a week and a day before the expected return of Christ. His obituary was printed in the Millerite paper *The Midnight Cry*. The description of Fitch's family in the last sentence of the obituary gives us a firsthand glimpse of why October 22 really was the "Great Disappointment" for those awaiting Christ's return. It reads, "His widow and fatherless children are now at Cleveland [Ohio], confidently expecting the coming of our Lord to gather the scattered members of the family."

One does not have to use a great deal of imagination to visualize what was happening there. You can almost hear the mother saying to her children, "Don't cry. Next Tuesday, when Jesus comes, we will see Daddy again." Since most families back then were large, and often one or more of the children died young—not to mention that the mothers themselves were more likely then than today to die in childbirth—the roots of their terrible disappointment become very apparent. Not only did Jesus not return and put their earthly troubles and pains to an end, but they were not reunited with their deceased loved ones. The day really did mark a great disappointment for them.

This powerful old hymn reminds us that Christ's promised return is sure. Even though His second coming has been delayed far beyond anything our pioneers ever foresaw, it urges us to continue to watch and work, for "Lo! He comes."

When Phoebe Palmer first wrote the hymn, it contained a sixth stanza:

> Lamb of God, Thou meek and lowly,
>   Judah's Lion high and holy,
> Lo, Thy bride comes forth to meet Thee,
>   All in blood-washed robes to greet Thee.

The tune used by the Millerites for this hymn is unknown. In fact, the hymn did not appear in any Seventh-day Adventist hymnal until 1886, when it was included in *Hymns and Tunes*. There it was set to the unnamed tune written by William James Kirkpatrick (1838-1921) that we still use today.

Watch, Ye Saints

Jude 15
Mrs. Phoebe Palmer, 1844 (1807-1874)
William J. Kirkpatrick (1838-1921)

1. Watch, ye saints, with eye - lids wak - ing; Lo! the powers of heaven are shak - ing;
2. Lo! the prom - ise of your Sav - ior, Par-doned sin and pur-chased fa - vor,
3. King-doms at their base are crumb-ling, Hark! His char - iot wheels are rum -bling;
4. Na - tions wane, tho' proud and state - ly; Christ His king - dom hast - eth great - ly;
5. Sin - ners, come, while Christ is plead -ing; Now for you He's in - ter - ced - ing;

Keep your lamps all trimmed and burn-ing, Read - y for your Lord's re - turn - ing.
Blood-washed robes and crowns of glo - ry; Haste to tell re - demp-tion's sto - ry.
Tell, O tell of grace a - bound-ing, While the sev - enth trump is sound-ing.
Earth her lat - est pangs is sum-ming; Shout, ye saints, your Lord is com - ing.
Haste, e'er grace and time di - min-ished Shall pro-claim the mys-tery fin - ished.

Refrain

Lo! He comes, Lo! Je-sus comes; Je -sus comes, He comes all glo-rious!

Je - sus comes, to reign vic- to - rious, Lo! He comes, yes, Je-sus comes!

WE'RE TRAVELING HOME

From the very start of William Miller's preaching, in 1831, inviting people to prepare to meet their soon-returning Saviour was a prominent part of his message. In fact, if any one thing surprised William Miller above all else, it was the negative, often hostile, reaction that so many people displayed toward his teaching that Christ would soon return. Miller fully expected that all the churches would welcome with open arms the idea that Christ was soon to return. He never understood the churches' hostility.

Early on, Miller would offer to pay a person to listen to a study of the Bible prophecies about Christ's second coming. That is more than most people do to share the news of Christ's soon return!

It happened that a doctor living near William Miller did not agree with Miller's interpretations of prophecy. Not only did the man disagree with Miller, he also felt that Miller was totally crazy on the subject. The doctor went around telling folk that Miller was a "monomaniac"; that is, he was sane on every subject except one. The physician claimed that if one happened to get Miller started talking on the prophecies, he would lose all his reason and become a raving lunatic.

It appears that William Miller had a sense of humor. The next time one of his children became ill, he called for this doctor to come check the child. After the doctor had finished examining Miller's child and giving a prescription, he turned to leave. Then he noticed William Miller sitting nearby, looking a bit downcast.

The physician inquired if something was wrong. Miller responded that he had heard it said that he, Miller, was a monomaniac. Miller wondered if the doctor could recognize a monomaniac if he saw one. When the doctor replied somewhat blushingly that he thought he could, William Miller asked the doctor to please examine him and then prescribe something for him if such was necessary. Miller told the doctor that he was willing to pay the normal fee for an examination.

Of course, the only way the doctor could tell whether Miller became a raving lunatic when talking about the prophecies was to listen to a Bible study on the topic! So William Miller began to go through the texts that showed the 2300-day prophecy would end sometime around 1843. As the doctor listened and then figured out the chronology, he saw that William Miller's calculations worked out perfectly.

Upon that revelation, the doctor became greatly agitated and left in a hurry. However, early the next morning he was back at Miller's home. He had spent a sleepless night because he realized that he was not ready to meet the Lord. William Miller studied more with the doctor for several days. According to the account, by the end of the studies the doctor was as much a monomaniac as William Miller. This certainly must have been one of the most unusual invitations that William Miller ever extended to anyone to get ready to meet the Lord.

In 1842 Joshua V. Himes issued a small throwaway-type hymnal called *Second Advent Hymns; Designed to Be Used in Prayer and Camp-Meetings.* It was also during 1842 that the Millerite Great Tent was constructed (described under "Together Let Us Sweetly Live") and the first of many Millerite camp meetings was held. Doubtless this small hymnal was issued for use at camp meetings and in the Great Tent. It contained no tunes at all—only the words. "We're Traveling Home" was one of the 19 hymns included in that small hymnal.

The hymn was also printed on the back page of the March 31, 1843, issue of *The Midnight Cry,* a Millerite paper. And Himes included it in both the 1842 and 1843 editions of the *Millennial Harp,* where it was called "Invitation."

James White printed three stanzas of the hymn in his 1855 and 1861 hymnals, also under the title "Invitation." He included stanzas 2 through 4 from Himes's book. The hymn was last reprinted by Seventh-day Adventists in the 1869 hymnal. There the first half of the first stanza only was changed, to read:

> We're going to see the heavenly King,
>> Will you go? Will you go?
> In rapturous strains His praise to sing,
>> Will you go? Will you go?

Stanzas 2 through 7 as published by Himes are included here. Himes's first stanza, with its problematic theology, which James White did not use, reads as follows:

We're trav'ling home to Heav'n above—
　　Will you go? Will you go?
To sing the Saviour's dying love—
　　Will you go? Will you go?
Millions have reach'd this blest abode,
　　Anointed kings and priests to God.
And millions now are on the road—
　　Will you go? Will you go?

We're Traveling Home

INVITATION

From Second Advent Hymns, *1842*

From Millenial Harp, *1842*

1. We're going to see the bleed - ing Lamb,
2. We're going to join the Heav'n - ly Choir, Will you go? Will you go?
3. Ye wea -ry, heav-y la - den come,

In rap-turous strains to praise His name, The
To raise our voice and tune the lyre, Will you go? Will you go? There
In the blest house there still is room, The

crown of life we there shall wear, The con-queror's palms our hands shall bear,
saints and an - gels glad - ly sing, Ho - sa - na to their God and King,
Lord is wait - ing to re - ceive. If thou wilt on Him now be - lieve,

And all the joys of heaven we'll share, Will you go? Will you go?
And make the heav'n-ly arch - es sing, Will you go? Will you go?
He'll give thy trou-bled con-science ease, Come be -lieve! Come be-lieve!

4. The way to heaven is free for all, Will you go? Will you go?
   For Jew and Gentile great and small, Will you go? Will you go?
Make up your mind, give God your heart,
   With every sin and idol part,
And now for glory, make a start, Come away! Come away!

5. The way to heaven is straight and plain, Will you go? Will you go?
   Repent, believe, be born again, Will you go? Will you go?
The Savior cries aloud to thee,
   "Take up thy cross and follow me,
And thou shalt My salvation see, Come to Me! Come to Me!"

6. O could I hear some sinner say, I will go! I will go!
   I'll start this moment, clear the way, Let me go! Let me go!
My old companions, fare you well,
   I will not go with you to hell,
I mean with Jesus Christ to dwell, Let me go! Fare you well!

YOU WILL SEE YOUR
LORD A-COMING

E arly on a January morning in 1843, James White, a 21-year-old fledgling Millerite Adventist, set out on his first preaching itinerary. It lasted four months. In his autobiography, *Life Incidents*, published in 1868, White recounts some of his experiences on that trip. He tells how his meetings were disrupted by other ministers who wanted to debate. He also recalls how he nearly froze as he rode from place to place on his horse through the winter snows of Maine. In one hall where he was lecturing on the prophecies, ruffians threw snowballs at him through the windows. But the Lord blessed his efforts and an estimated 1,000 people traced their conversions to James White's preaching those four months.

It was during that trip that James White used this particular hymn that was popular with the Millerites to good effect. He says: "Litchfield Plains was my next place of labor. The house was crowded the first evening. In fact, it was with difficulty that I found my way to the pulpit. To call the people to order, the first words they heard from me were in singing,

> 'You will see your Lord a-coming,
> You will see your Lord a-coming,
> You will see your Lord a-coming,
>   In a few more days,
>   While a band of music,
>   While a band of music,
>   While a band of music,
> Shall be chanting through the air!'

"The reader certainly cannot see poetic merit in the repetition of these simple lines. And if he has never heard the sweet melody to which they were attached, he will be at a loss to see how one voice could employ them so as to hold nearly a thousand persons in almost breathless silence. But it is a fact that there was in those days a power in what was called [Millerite] Advent singing, such as was felt in no other" (*Life Incidents*, p. 94).

(For another story about James White starting a meeting by

singing as he walked down the aisle, clapping his Bible to keep time, see under "When I Can Read My Title Clear.")

Not everyone in Litchfield Plains accepted the Millerite message of Christ's soon return. Sometime later, after his ordination, James White went through there on another preaching trip. He met a minister who had opposed his work during his first visit. James recalled, "I met this minister in the road, and as we passed he seemed to be surprised to meet me again, and said, 'Why, Mr. White, are you yet in the land of the living?' 'No, sir,' was the reply, 'I am in the land of the dying, but at the soon coming of the Lord, I expect to go to the land of the living.' We each went our way" (*ibid.*, p. 108).

James White recalled another meeting about the same time that was held in Knox, Maine. He and two of his sisters were present. Again this hymn figures in the story.

"At the close of [the] service, the Lord's Supper was to be celebrated, and while the friends of Jesus were gathering around His table, I joined with my sisters in singing, 'You will see your Lord a coming. . . .' As we would strike the chorus of each verse, 'With a band of music,' a good Brother Clark, who ever seemed to have resting upon him a solemn sense of the great day of God near at hand, would rise, strike his hands together over his head, shout 'Glory!' and immediately sit down. A more solemn appearing man I never saw. Each repetition of this chorus would bring Brother Clark to his feet, and call from him the same shout of glory. The Spirit of God came upon the brethren, who by this time were seated ready to receive the emblems of our dying Lord. The influence of the melody, accompanied by Brother Clark's solemn appearance and sweet shouts, seemed electrifying. Many were in tears, while responses of 'Amen' and 'Praise the Lord' were heard from almost everyone who loved the Advent hope. The emblems were passed, and that . . . meeting closed" (*ibid.*, p. 107).

The first appearance of "You Will See Your Lord a-Coming" in Adventist hymnals was its publication in the *Small Second Advent Hymns; Designed to Be Used in Prayer and Camp-Meetings*, published by Joshua V. Himes in 1842. Himes also included the hymn in the 1843 edition of *Millennial Harp*. There it had nine stanzas. Variations of this hymn were later printed in the Seventh-day Adventist hymnals down to and including *Hymns and Tunes*, published in 1886. The 1985 *Seventh-day Adventist Hymnal* has once again included it—this time in the "Early Advent" hymn section, but with only five stanzas.

The original stanzas not presently included are:

3. He'll awake all the nations,
   He'll awake all the nations,
  He'll awake all the nations,
    From the old church-yards,

4. There will be a mighty wailing,
   There will be a mighty wailing,
  There will be a mighty wailing,
    At the old church-yards,

5. O sinner, will you tremble,
   O sinner, will you tremble,
  O sinner, will you tremble,
    At the old church-yards,

6. You will flee to rocks and mountains,
   You will flee to rocks and mountains,
  You will flee to rocks and mountains,
    From the old church-yards.

If one wishes to sing the hymn in *Early Advent Singing* as originally printed by Himes, rather than using the phrase "In a few more days" at the end of each stanza, the ending needs to be varied. Stanza 1 should end with "While the old church-yards . . . "; stanza 2, "Through the old church-yards . . . "; and the remaining stanzas should end with "From the old church-yards."

You Will See Your Lord a-Coming

From Millenial Harp, *1843*   *Early Advent hymn sung by James White*

1. You will   see your Lord a - com - ing, You will   see your Lord a -
2. Ga -briel sounds his might-y   trum - pet, Ga - briel   sounds his might - y
3. You will   see the saints a - ris - ing, You will   see the saints a -
4. An - gels bear them to the   Sav - ior, An - gels   bear them to the
5. Then we'll shout, our suff'rings   o - ver, Then we'll   shout, our suf-ferings

com-ing, You will   see your Lord a   com-ing
trum-pet, Ga -briel   sounds his might -y   trum - pet
ris - ing, You will   see the saints a - ris - ing   In   a   few   more   days.
Sav -ior, An -gels   bear them to the   Sav -ior
o - ver, Then we'll shout, our suf-f'rings   o - ver

Refrain

Hear the   band   of   mu - sic, Hear the   band   of
(heav'n-ly band)   (heav'n-ly band)

mu-sic, Hear the   band   Of   mu - sic which is sound-ing thro' the   air.
(heav'n-ly band)

71

PIONEER SABBATHKEEPING ADVENTIST HYMNS

1845-1863

PIONEER SABBATHKEEPING ADVENTIST HYMNS

The hymns included in this section are selected from those sung by early Sabbathkeepers between the disappointment of October 22, 1844, and the founding of the General Conference of Seventh-day Adventists in Battle Creek, Michigan, on May 21, 1863. During this formative period, the pioneers sang both Millerite hymns and others that reflected the new doctrines being adopted by the emerging church. The words of some hymns had to be changed to bring them into agreement with the new church's doctrinal beliefs. In addition, original hymns were written by such members as Annie Smith, Heman S. Gurney, Uriah Smith, and Roswell F. Cottrell, to mention a few of the better-known names.

During those years James White was the major compiler of hymnals used by Sabbathkeepers. A total of five hymnals and four supplements were published prior to 1863. They are as follows:

1849	*Hymns for God's Peculiar People That Keep the Commandments of God and the Faith of Jesus*, 53 hymns on 48 pages.
1852	*Hymns for Second Advent Believers Who Observe the Sabbath of the Lord*, 139 hymns on 112 pages.
1853	*Supplement to Advent and Sabbath Hymns*, 38 hymns on 32 pages.
1854	*Hymns for Youth and Children* (compiled by Anna White), 117 hymns on 82 pages.
1855	*Hymns for Those Who Keep the Commandments of God and the Faith of Jesus*, 474 hymns on 352 pages.
1858	*Supplement*, 75 hymns on 94 pages.
1860	*Addition to the Supplement*, 8 hymns on 16 pages.
1861	*Hymns for Those Who Keep the Commandments of God and the Faith of Jesus*, 529 hymns on 464 pages.
1863	*The Sabbath Lute*, 42 hymns on 48 pages.

The first three hymnals contained no music—only the words. It was not until the 1855 *Hymns for Those Who Keep the*

Commandments of God that music was provided for some of the hymns. It is also interesting that the first book of any size that James White published was not a doctrinal work, nor was it his wife Ellen's visions, but rather the 1849 *Hymns for God's Peculiar People.* Though dated 1849, that first hymnal was actually not available until March of 1850, when it was advertised in *The Present Truth* for 12½ cents each, or 12 copies for $1. James White's second hymnal, the 1852 *Hymns for Second Advent Believers*, was the first hardbound book ever published by Sabbathkeepers.

Since the earliest hymnals contained no music and the Sabbathkeeping pioneers did not use musical instruments in their churches during those early years, the quality of singing suffered. One solution was to put religious words to secular tunes of the day. (See comments about this practice under "O Brother, Be Faithful.") Several illustrations of this are included in *Early Advent Singing.*

For a more complete treatment of early Adventist hymns, see the historical introductory chapter in *Companion to the Seventh-day Adventist Hymnal,* by Wayne Hooper and Edward E. White.

The following is a list of additional hymns that were introduced into Adventist hymnody during the years of 1849 to 1863 that can still be found in the 1985 *Seventh-day Adventist Hymnal.* In some cases the words have varied slightly through the years, or the current tunes are not the same as those originally used. The year preceding each hymn indicates the hymnal that first contained the song. The title is followed by the hymn number in the 1985 hymnal. Those hymns with an asterisk are also included in *Early Advent Singing.*

1855	All Hail the Power of Jesus' Name	SDAH 229
1855	Am I a Soldier of the Cross?	609
1861	Angels From the Realms of Glory	119
1855	Awake, My Soul!	611
1860	Beautiful Zion, Built Above	450
1855	Blest Be the Tie 350	
1855	Come, Holy Spirit, Heavenly Dove	269
1863	Come, Thou Fount of Every Blessing	334
1855	Day of Judgment, Day of Wonders!	418
1854	Don't You See My Jesus Coming?	*454
	(also sung by the Millerites)	
1852	From Every Stormy Wind That Blows	*527
	(Alternate title: The Mercy Seat)	

[†] The Millerites sang this hymn as "Must Simon bear his cross alone?" The words were considerably altered throughout the hymn, and the tune was different. The original words and tune were also used in Seventh-day Adventist hymnals as late as *Hymns and Tunes*, published in 1886, No. 1173.

GOD OF MY LIFE

I t seemed that everything in George I. Butler's (1834-1918) life
was changing. In 1888 he tried to stop the preaching of what to
him sounded like strange new doctrine. But to no avail.

Stunned, embittered, and discouraged, this resolute defender of
the faith retired to a farm in Florida, on which he planted an orange
grove. For 13 years, until his ailing wife died, Elder Butler remained
in virtual isolation from his former colleagues. It appeared his work
for the church was over.

Butler was born November 12, 1834, in Waterbury, Vermont, the
son of a starch manufacturer and grandson of a Vermont governor.
When his parents became Sabbathkeepers, he did not. A skeptic,
George found only contradictions in the Bible.

In 1856, however, a thought came to him as if spoken by an
audible voice: *There are some good things in the Bible; why not believe
that part anyway?* He looked up and said, "I'll do it, Lord," and felt an
immediate change come over him. Within a few months George
returned home to Iowa, where his parents were then living, and was
baptized by J. N. Andrews.

Now a converted young man, George taught school for two
winters near his home. At the age of 24 he married Lentha A.
Lockwood. The newlyweds settled on a farm, where a daughter and
two sons were born to them.

Although unordained at the time, this farmer-layman was elected
president of the Iowa Conference in 1865. Ordination came two
years later at the hands of James White and D. T. Bourdeau. While
still serving as president of the Iowa Conference, George was
simultaneously elected president of the General Conference. In this
new post he crisscrossed the country by train from Maine to
California, attending camp meetings and church councils, building
institutions, and chairing their boards. In 1874 he helped raise
money to establish both the Pacific Press Publishing Association and
Battle Creek College. In 1884 he went to Europe—he was the first
incumbent General Conference president to travel outside the
United States. He spent more than a year in Europe, during which
time he helped to establish three publishing houses.

Noted for his forceful will, this church administrator also
possessed a keen, analytical mind. Unfortunately, he was also known

for his irascibility and distrust of others. His years of retirement, with time for contemplation (during which Ellen White remained a close friend and pleaded with him to change his views), did much to cleanse him of these characteristics. Shortly after the turn of the century, he was elected president of the Southern Union, a position he held until 1907.

In 1915 this re-retired but still active worker attended the Fall Council at Loma Linda, California, where leaders debated whether to spend funds to get their fledgling medical school accredited or close it and put the money into missions. Since none felt the mission program should be curtailed, it seemed the medical school would have to be closed.

General Conference president A. G. Daniells was about to call for the vote when 80-year-old Butler asked to speak. His speech went something like this: "You know that at times I have not always been on the right side of situations. Although it has taken awhile, I have learned not to vote against what God has told us we should do. Sister White has made it clear that we should have this medical school, and now before her body is barely cold in the grave [Ellen White had died in July of that year] we are talking about closing it. I want to say that when the chairman calls for the vote, this is one old hand that will not go up in favor of the motion."

When Elder Daniells called for the vote, the motion to close the medical school at Loma Linda was defeated.

On July 25, 1918—just a few months after attending the General Conference session in San Francisco—G. I. Butler died of a brain tumor, in Healdsburg, California. During the last years of his life he was often heard singing William Cowper's old hymn:

> Poor though I am, despised, forgot,
> Yet God, my God, forgets me not;
> And he is safe and must succeed
> For whom the Lord vouchsafes to plead.

During his last illness, while lying in bed, this church patriarch was heard to exclaim, "O my God, how much I love Thee!" This was not the same person who in 1888 had taken a firm stand against the preaching of righteousness by faith in Christ by A. T. Jones and E. J. Waggoner at the Minneapolis General Conference session. Slowly, very slowly, Butler had grown to see the importance of making Christ central in preaching and doctrine. Behind his iron will beat a kind and loving heart, repentant of mistakes and sins, tender in sympathy, and strong in love for God and humanity.

George I. Butler, the man who had done so much for his church during the 11 years he served as General Conference president (1871-1874, 1880-1888), only to feel rejected because of "strange new doctrine," finally came to know Christ fully.

God of My Life

From Hymns and Tunes, *1886*
William Cowper (1731-1800)

MILLER
C. P. E. Bach (1714-1788)

1. God of my life, to Thee, I call, Af-flict-ed
2. Friend of the friend-less and the faint, Where shall I
3. Did ev-er mourn-er plead with Thee, And Thou re-
4. Poor though I am, de-spised, for-got, Yet God, my

at Thy feet I fall; When the great wa-ter-
lodge my deep com-plaint? Where but with Thee whose
fuse that mourn-er's plea? Does not the word still
God, for-gets me not; And he is safe and

floods pre-vail, Leave not my tremb-ling heart to fail.
o-pen door In-vites the help-less and the poor?
fixed re-main, That none shall seek Thy face in vain?
must suc-ceed For whom the Lord vouch-safes to plead.

HE SLEEPS IN JESUS

One of the distinctive biblical doctrines that the emerging group of Sabbathkeepers adopted was that of the unconscious state of a person in death, otherwise known as conditional immortality. It was George Storrs (1796-1879) who had earlier introduced this topic to the Millerite Adventists. Though most of the leaders of that movement argued against Storrs's view, Charles Fitch came out in favor of it in January 1844.

Among our own Sabbathkeeping pioneers, all three of the cofounders of the Seventh-day Adventist Church, Joseph Bates and James and Ellen White, accepted the biblical teaching on the state of the dead. Among the doctrinal errors that James White watched for as he prepared his early hymnals were references to the dead being in heaven.

At the time James White published his first hymnal in 1849, he was only 28. That first book contained no funeral hymns, though it did contain one hymn about the resurrection. It was not until the *Supplement to the Advent and Sabbath Hymns* was published in 1853 that two funeral hymns were actually included. One of those two hymns, "Asleep in Jesus!" (not to be confused with "He Sleeps in Jesus"), continued to be included in Seventh-day Adventist hymnals down through the 1941 *Church Hymnal*.

Annie R. Smith, the talented older sister of Uriah Smith, wrote the hymn "He Sleeps in Jesus" in honor of Robert F. Harmon, Jr., Ellen White's older brother. He died of tuberculosis on February 5, 1853, at the age of 27. (Annie's story is told under the hymn "How Far From Home?") When the poem was first published in the *Review and Herald* with his obituary sketch, there was no indication that it was intended as a hymn. But later it was published with music in the 1855 hymnal. The hymn tune REST that was used originally was written by William B. Bradbury in 1843 and is the tune used in *Early Advent Singing*. In the 1886 *Hymns and Tunes*, the words were set to the tune RUSSELL, written by Edwin Barnes. The newer tune was also used when "He Sleeps in Jesus" was last published in the 1941 *Church Hymnal* (No. 494).

Robert Harmon, Jr., was the sixth child in a family of eight. Only his twin sisters, Ellen and Elizabeth, were younger. As a young man he had accepted the Millerite teachings and looked for Christ's return in 1844 along with the rest of his family. After the disappointment of October 22, 1844, he lost interest in the second coming of Christ, though he still tried to live a Christian life. As with so many others among those who had been disappointed, it was a very difficult time for Robert.

Though his older sister, Sarah (Harmon) Belden, accepted the Sabbath, and in time so did his parents, Robert and Eunice Harmon, young Robert apparently did not do so until just before his death. In July 1852 he contracted tuberculosis. As he faced the reality that he probably would not live long, he spent much time in prayer. Once again his faith in the second coming of Christ revived and for the first time he also saw the beauty of the Sabbath, and greatly rejoiced in it.

When word of Robert's illness reached James and Ellen White, who were living in Rochester, New York, they decided to visit him at his parents' home in Gorham, Maine. Though he was emaciated from the tuberculosis that was ravaging his body, Ellen observed that her brother's wasted features lit up with joy as they talked of the bright hope of the future. It was a sad parting when a short time later she and James had to leave to continue visiting churches. Doubtless Ellen reflected back on their 10 years when together they had accepted Millerism and looked for Christ's soon return. Both she and Robert had tried to share their newfound faith with their Methodist Bible class, but their witness generally fell on uninterested ears. As Robert had tried to speak in his meek yet clear way, his touching manner caused some to weep and be moved, but others just coughed dissentingly and seemed quite uneasy. After Robert's death, the last stanza of Annie Smith's poem, "He Sleeps in Jesus," was inscribed on his tombstone.

Little could Annie Smith guess as she wrote this poem to eulogize Robert Harmon that in just over two years she too would be dead of the same disease. In the meantime she wrote poems for several other young Sabbathkeepers who died in the hope of the resurrection. Included among them were James White's brother Nathaniel White, in 1853, and his sister Anna White, in 1854, as well as Lumen V. Masten, foreman in the Review office at Rochester, who also died in 1854. All were in their 20s when they died. With each additional death, the hope of the resurrection was becoming ever more meaningful to those early Adventists.

He Sleeps in Jesus

REST (BRADBURY)

Annie R. Smith, 1853 (1828-1855)   *William B. Bradbury, 1843 (1816-1868*

1. He sleeps in Je - sus peace-ful rest   No mor-tal strife in - vades his breast
2. He lived, his Sav - ior to a - dore, And meekly all his suf-ferings bore:
3. Does earth at - tract thee here? they cried The dy -ing Chris-tian thus re - plied,
4. He sleeps in Je - sus soon to rise, When the last trump shall rend the skies;
5. He sleeps in Je - sus cease thy grief; Let this af - ford thee sweet re - lief

No pain, nor sin, nor woe, nor care, Can reach the si - lent slumberer there.
He loved, and all re - signed to God; Nor murmured at His chastening rod.
While point-ing up-ward to the sky, My trea-sure is laid up on high.
Then burst the fet -ters of the tomb, To wake in full im - mor-tal bloom
That, freed from death's tri-umph and reign, In hea -ven he will live a - gain.

85

HOW FAR FROM HOME?

Annie Smith, the older sister of Uriah Smith, had already written several hymns before "How Far From Home?" was first published in *The Advent Review and Sabbath Herald* of November 29, 1853. Accompanying its publication was a note that it was to be sung to the tune of "Tis Midnight Hour," a well-known, though anonymously written, popular song. This is an example of writing religious words for a secular tune. (See comments about this practice under "O Brother, Be Faithful.")

The original words for "Tis Midnight Hour" are:

> 1. 'Tis midnight hour, the moon shines bright,
>   The dewdrops blaze beneath her ray,
>   The twinkling stars their trembling light
>   Like beauty's eyes display.

> Chorus:
>   Then sleep no more, tho' round thy heart
>   Some tender heart may idly play,
>   For midnight song with magic art
>   Shall chase that dream away.

> 2. 'Tis midnight hour, from flow'r to flow'r
>   The wayward zephyr floats along,
>   Or lingers in the shaded bow'r,
>   To hear the nightbird's song.

As a girl Annie Smith had been a Millerite Adventist along with members of her family. Her interest in the second coming of Christ declined after the disappointment of October 22, 1844. She decided to pursue an education along literary and artistic lines. Annie trained to be a teacher at the Charlestown Female Seminary in Charlestown, Massachusetts, near Boston. She had several poems published in *The Ladies' Wreath*, a literary magazine printed in New York. One day while sketching the Boston skyline from Prospect Hill in Somerville, she strained her eyes so badly that for about eight months she could not use them.

Annie's mother, Rebekah Smith, was concerned for the spiritual welfare of her daughter. When in 1851 Mrs. Smith heard that Joseph Bates was going to be holding meetings near where Annie lived, she invited her daughter to attend them. To please her mother, Annie decided she would go.

The night before the meetings were to open, Annie had a remarkable dream. It seemed she arrived late at a meeting only to discover there were no seats left in the hall, except one in the last row. In her dream the minister was speaking on the sanctuary question.

Joseph Bates had a similar dream that same night. In it he saw a young girl arrive late and sit in the very last row of the meeting hall. It was also indicated to him that he should change from his planned topic of the evening—the prophecies of Daniel—and speak instead on the sanctuary and the passing of the time in 1844, the Sabbath, and the third angel's message.

The next evening, much to her surprise, Annie found herself acting out her dream. Thinking to have left plenty early, she lost her way and found herself arriving late—with nowhere to sit except in the last row. And up in front was the man she had seen preaching in her dream. As can be imagined, when the meeting was over, Annie Smith and Joseph Bates had much to talk about. Within days she accepted the Sabbath and sent off the first of a number of poems that she would write for the *Review and Herald*. It was called "Fear Not, Little Flock" and was published in the September 16, 1851, issue.

James White immediately asked her to join him in editing the paper, but she declined because of her poor eyesight. However, she later joined the Whites in Saratoga Springs, New York. After prayer, her eyesight improved. Then in 1852 she moved with them when they transferred the paper to Rochester, New York. Unfortunately, this extremely talented young woman contracted tuberculosis, so she returned to her home in West Wilton, New Hampshire, in the hopes of regaining her health. While there she edited a book of her poems that was published after her death, at the age of 27, on July 26, 1855. One of the hymns that she included in her book was "How Far From Home?"

Though not the first hymn writer among the early Sabbathkeepers, Annie Smith was one of the first, and certainly the most prolific.

When Annie wrote her hymn "How Far From Home?" it originally had an additional stanza:

How far from home? ah, then, I cried
    To God, who marks each plaintive sigh:
A still, small voice, within replied,
    Not far from home am I!
Then weep no more, though round thy way
    Afflictions rise, and doubt and fear,
While myriad voices secretly say,
    The pilgrim's home is near.

    James White first included the hymn in his 1855 hymnal. Through the years it has continued to be retained in subsequent Adventist hymnals.

How Far From Home?

Annie R. Smith, 1853 (1828-1855   TIS MIDNIGHT HOUR

1. How   far from home? I asked, as on I   bent my steps-the watchman spake
2. I   asked the war-rior on the field; This was his soul -in - spir - ing song:
3. I   asked a - gain; earth, sea, and sun Seemed, with one voice to make re -ply:
4. Not   far from home! O bless-ed tho't! The trav-'ler's lone-ly heart to cheer;

"The   long, dark night is al - most gone, The morn-ing soon will break.
"With   cour -age, bold, the sword I'll wield, The bat - tle is   not   long.
"Time's wast -ing sands are near - ly run, E - ter - ni - ty   is   nigh.
Which   oft   a heal-ing balm has bro't, And dried the mourn-er's tear.

Then   weep no more, but speed thy flight, With Hope's brite star thy guid -ing ray,
Then   weep no more, but well en -dure The con - flict, till thy work is done:
Then   weep no more-with warn-ing tones, Por - ten -tious signs are thick'ning round,
Then   weep no more, since we shall meet Where wea - ry footsteps nev - er roam--

Till   thou shalt reach the realms of light In ev - er -last - ing day."
For   this we know, the prize is sure, When vic - to - ry   is   won."
The   whole cre - a - tion, wait -ing, groans, To hear the trum - pet sound."
Our   tri - als past, our joys com-plete, Safe in our Fa - ther's home.

89

I SAW ONE WEARY

Annie Smith wrote this poem on August 19, 1852. At the time, she was living in Rochester, New York, with James and Ellen White and the others who were working together to publish the paper called *The Advent Review and Sabbath Herald*. (See Annie's story under "How Far From Home?") Since her poem is dated August 19 and the issue of the paper that it is printed in is also dated August 19, it would seem that she must have written it the same day it was published. Her other poems published elsewhere in the same volume of the *Review and Herald* carry the dates she wrote them—generally one or more days before the paper was published. However quickly Annie may have written this particular poem, the words have come down to us unchanged from when they were first printed.

The August 19, 1852, issue of the *Review and Herald* is significant in Adventist history because it also contained James White's notice that he was starting a paper for young people entitled *The Youth's Instructor*. In that issue of the *Review*, James White reproduced the entire front page of his new monthly youth paper. The first issue was dated August, 1852. He said that it would be sent free to those who could not pay, though others were asked to contribute toward its publication. *The Youth's Instructor* was published from 1852 to 1970, when it was replaced by *Insight*.

When "I Saw One Weary" was first published, it was called "The Blessed Hope." There was no indication that it was designed to be a hymn, though by 1853 it was included in the *Supplement* that was issued that year to the 1852 hymnal. Since no music was printed with the hymnal until the 1855 hymnal, it can only be assumed that the words must have been set to music shortly after they were written. Even more likely, Annie had the tune in mind as she wrote the words. The hymn has been retained in our hymnals to the present.

Traditionally it has been thought that Annie had specific individuals in mind as she wrote each of the first three stanzas of "I Saw One Weary." The first is generally thought to be about Joseph Bates (1792-1872), the retired sea captain turned apostle of the Sabbath truth who became one of the three cofounders of the Seventh-day Adventist Church. Since he was the patriarch of the group—being nearly 30 years older than James White—the reference to the lines of grief and care that were furrowed upon his brow would indicate that someone older was being described. Bates long had borne the cross, first as a Millerite Adventist and then as the oldest leader in the group that started the Seventh-day Adventist Church.

The second stanza has traditionally been held to refer to the experience of James White (1821-1881), another cofounder of the Seventh-day Adventist Church. He was the dynamic leader of the group—the promoter and builder who seemed always to be on the go with some new idea or way to push forward the work of God.

The third stanza has been understood to refer to John N. Andrews (1829-1883), the denomination's first official missionary. Others have suggested that Annie was possibly referring to her younger brother, Uriah Smith. This second possibility seems highly unlikely since Uriah had not yet started to keep the Sabbath when his sister wrote the poem. In fact Uriah did not become a Sabbathkeeper until December 1852. Some have also questioned the identification of Andrews as the person, since he did not leave behind "cherished friends" until 1874, when he was sent out as a missionary—22 years after the poem was written.

But before giving up on him too quickly as the one Annie had in mind, it should be recalled that John Andrews' uncle, Charles Andrews, was a member of Congress and had tried to get his brilliant young nephew to study law and go into politics. Since John gave up all this to join an unknown group of Sabbathkeepers who did not even have a name as of yet and had no church structure, his experience could at least partially qualify him as the one described by Annie in her poem.

According to a tradition in the Leonard Hastings family, there is another possible identification. It was their belief that Annie Smith was referring to her own experience, though modesty caused her to disguise that fact by her use of the masculine pronouns throughout the stanza. Annie also had given up what she felt was a promising artistic and literary career to become a Sabbathkeeper. The fact that the Hastings were the closest Sabbathkeeping neighbors to the Smith family gives weight to this tradition.

Whether the stanza refers to John Andrews or Annie Smith herself, the experience talked about is similar to that of countless thousands who since then have given up family, friends, and fortune when they discovered the Adventist faith.

It is agreed that the fourth stanza refers to the experience of church members at large. Without a doubt, the "blessed hope" should buoy the spirits of all who claim the name Seventh-day Adventist.

I Saw One Weary

Titus 2:13
Annie R. Smith, 1852 (1828-1855)

DUANE STREET
George Coles, 1835 (1792-1858)

1. I saw one wea-ry, sad, and torn, With ea-ger steps press on the way,
2. And one I saw, with sword and shield, Who bold-ly braved the world's cold frown,
3. And there was one who left be-hind The cher-ished friends of ear-ly years,
4. While pil-grims here we jour-ney on In this dark vale of sin and gloom,

Who long the hal-lowed cross had borne, Still look-ing for the prom-ised day;
And fought, un-yield-ing, on the field, To win an ev-er-last-ing crown.
And hon-or, pleas-ure, wealth re-signed, To tread the path be-dewed with tears.
Through trib-u-la-tion, hate, and scorn, Or through the por-tals of the tomb,

While man-y a line of grief and care Up-on his brow was fur-rowed there;
Though worn with toil, op-pressed by foes, No mur-mur from his heart a-rose;
Through tri-als deep and con-flicts sore Yet still a smile of joy he wore;
Till our re-turn-ing King shall come To take His ex-ile cap-tives home,

I asked what buoyed his spir-its up, "O this!" said he-- "the bless-ed hope."
I asked what buoyed his spir-its up, "O this!" said he-- "the bless-ed hope."
I asked what buoyed his spir-its up, "O this!" said he-- "the bless-ed hope."
O! what can buoy the spir-its up? 'Tis this a-lone-- the bless-ed hope.

I'M BUT A STRANGER HERE

Thomas Rawson Taylor (1807-1835) wrote the words to this hymn in 1835. Born in England, he was the son of a Congregational minister. At the age of 18 Taylor entered college to train for the Congregational ministry. Upon completion of his education he served briefly as a pastor until ill health forced him to resign. Later he taught school. His death occurred at the premature age of 27 in 1835. The hymn contains three references to Taylor's impending death: "Short is my pilgrimage"; "Time's . . . blast soon will be overpast"; and "I soon shall rest."

In 1854 Lowell Mason (1792-1872) composed the tune OAK especially for these words. Undoubtedly, the early pioneers who sang this hymn knew nothing about the author's background. In fact, the *Supplement* to the 1855 hymnal that James White brought out in 1858, and which was the first Adventist hymnal to contain this hymn, did not name either its author or composer. For the early pioneers, this hymn spoke only about the trials and troubles they were experiencing here on earth as they looked forward to their real home in heaven, not someone else's experience. The hymn has been reprinted in Adventist hymnals to the present time, including the current *Seventh-day Adventist Hymnal*.

The references in the second stanza to "the tempest rage" and to "Time's cold and wintry blast" bring to mind stories of the terrible winter conditions that our New England Adventist pioneers had to endure in the early days of this movement. Joseph Bates, a generation older than most of the other pioneers, thought nothing at all about starting out on preaching trips in the dead of winter. Often he tramped many long miles to look up a single family. Weather seemed no deterrent to him. When 65 years of age, he baptized seven people in a river. That in itself was not so unusual. But Bates was standing in a hole cut through three feet of ice, and the temperature was reported to be 30 degrees below zero!

In early November 1856 James and Ellen White found themselves in Round Grove, Illinois. Elon Everts and Josiah Hart, friends from New England, had moved there. For a month the Whites stayed in Round Grove while holding meetings.

Other Adventist families had also moved West—to Waukon, Iowa—to take up farming. The Andrews and Stevens families of

Paris, Maine, had moved to Waukon, and the J. N. Loughborough family had joined them there. This removed from the work two young and successful ministers, J. N. Andrews and J. N. Loughborough. Among other things, the group was upset over the move of the *Advent Review* office from Rochester, New York, to Battle Creek, Michigan, a year earlier. And so in their discouragement, Andrews and Loughborough had left the ministry to take up farming with the others.

On Tuesday, December 9, Ellen White was given a vision while still in Round Grove. She tells about what happened next in the first edition of her autobiography, *Spiritual Gifts*, volume 2, published in 1860.

"I was shown the state of those brethren who had moved to Wawkon [Waukon], Iowa. Nearly all of them were in darkness, opposed to the work of God. . . . Satan had planted the seeds of dissatisfaction, and the front was ripening. . . .

"I saw that they needed help, that Satan's snare must be broken, and precious souls rescued. I did not see that it was our duty to go to them, but as I had been shown their condition, I felt anxious to go. It was a great distance, and in the winter. It was exceedingly difficult, and somewhat dangerous a journey, yet I felt urged to go to Wawkon. My mind could not be at ease until we decided to go trusting in the Lord. It was then good sleighing. Preparations were made to go with two horses and a sleigh, but it rained for 24 hours, and the snow was fast disappearing. My husband thought the journey west must be given up. My mind could not rest. It was agitated concerning Wawkon.

"Bro. H[art] said to me, 'Sr. White, what about Wawkon?'

"Said I, 'We shall go.'

" 'Yes,' said he, 'if the Lord works a miracle.' Many times that night I was at the window watching the weather, and about daybreak there was a change, and it commenced snowing. The next night about five o'clock, we were on our way to Wawkon, brethren E[verts] and H[art], husband and self. We held meetings with the brethren at Green Vale, Ills., and were there blocked in nearly a week with a severe snowstorm. Thursday we ventured to pursue our journey. Weary, cold and hungry, we called at a hotel a few miles from the Mississippi River. The next morning, about four o'clock, it commenced raining. We felt urged to go on, and rode through the rain, while the horses broke through the snow at almost every step.

We made many inquiries about crossing the river, but none gave us encouragement that we could cross. The ice was mostly composed of snow, and there lay upon the top of it one foot of water. When we reached the river Bro. H[art] arose in the sleigh and said, 'Is it Iowa, or back to Illinois? We have come to the Red Sea, shall we cross?' We answered, 'Go forward, trusting in Israel's God.' We ventured upon the ice, praying as we went. We were carried safely across, and as we ascended the Iowa bank of the river, we united in praising the Lord. A number told us after we crossed, that no amount of money would have tempted them to cross, and that a number had broken in. They could not save their teams, and barely escaped with their lives. We rode that afternoon six miles from Dubuque. The Sabbath was drawing on, and we put up at a hotel to rest over the Sabbath. . . .

"Sunday, we continued our journey. I never witnessed so cold weather. The brethren would watch each other to see if they were freezing. And we would often hear, 'Brother, your face is freezing, you had better rub the frost out as soon as possible!' 'Your ear is freezing!' 'Your nose is freezing!' I found my coon-skin robe of real service.

"We reached Wawkon Wednesday night, and found nearly all of the Sabbathkeepers sorry that we had come" (pp. 217-219).

Many years later J. N. Loughborough recalled his surprised reaction to the Whites' arrival in Waukon:

"One day about Christmastime, in December, as Brother Hosea Mead and I were working on a store building in Waukon, a man looking up saw me, and inquired, 'Do you know a carpenter around here by the name of Hosea Mead?'

"I replied, 'Yes, sir, he is up here working with me.'

"Brother Mead said, 'That is Elon Evert's voice.'

"Then he came and looked down, and Brother Everts said, 'Come down; Brother and Sister White and Brother Hart are out here in the sleigh.'

"As I reached the sleigh, Sister White greeted me with the question, 'What *doest* thou here, Elijah?'

"Astonished at such a question, I replied, 'I am working with Brother Mead at carpenter work.'

"The second time she repeated, 'What doest *thou* here, Elijah?'

"Now I was so embarrassed at such a question, and the connecting of my case with 'Elijah,' that I did not know what to say. It was evident that there was something back of all this which I should hear more about.

"The third time she repeated the question, 'What doest thou here, Elijah?'

"I was brought by these bare questions to very seriously consider the case of Elijah, away from the direct work of the Lord, hid in a cave. As our meetings by them progressed, I learned that she was instructed, in a vision at Round Grove, to salute me, when she should meet me, in that very manner. I can assure you . . . , that the salutation most thoroughly convinced me that there was going to come a change, and a 'go back' from the labor in which I was then engaged" (*Pacific Union Recorder*, Aug. 4, 1910; see also A. L. White, *Ellen G. White: The Early Years*, pp. 348, 349).

At the end of the meetings in Waukon, both J. N. Loughborough and J. N. Andrews decided to reenter the active ministry. Neither of them ever again looked back as long as they lived. But rather, both gave the work of God their all, because "There, too, I soon shall rest; heaven is my home."

I'm But a Stranger Here

OAK

Thomas R. Taylor, 1835 (1807-1835) *Lowell Mason, 1854 (1792-1872)*

1. I'm but a stran - ger here, Earth is a des - ert drear, Dan - ger and sor - row stand Round me on ev - ery hand; Heaven is my Fa - ther - land, Heaven is my home;

2. What though the temp - est rage, Short is my pil - grim - age, Time's cold and win - try blast Soon will be o - ver - past; I shall reach home at last; Heaven is my home;

3. There at my Sav - ior's side, I shall be glo - ri - fied, There'll be the good and blest, Those I love most and best, There, too, I soon shall rest; Heaven is my home.

LAND OF LIGHT

This hymn was written by Uriah Smith, long-time editor of *The Adventist Review and Sabbath Herald*. It was first published in the January 24, 1856, issue of that paper, with instructions that it should be sung to the tune of "Old Folks at Home." The hymn was later reprinted in the *Supplement* to the 1855 hymnal published in 1858.

The songs of Stephen Foster were sweeping America at the time Uriah Smith chose to write religious words for this popular tune. As with other hymns set to popular tunes of the day (for a discussion of this practice, see under "O Brother, Be Faithful"), when the tunes have continued to be known in popular society, generally they have not been retained in our subsequent hymnals. "Land of Light" is such a hymn. It was never reprinted.

Uriah Smith became a Sabbathkeeper in 1852. His first contribution to Adventist literature was a 35,000-word poem entitled "The Warning Voice of Time and Prophecy," which ran in the *Review and Herald* for five months in 1853. In 1855 he was invited to become editor of the paper after its move from Rochester, New York, to Battle Creek, Michigan. He retained that position for the majority of the time until his death in 1903.

Before the move from Rochester, it was decided to bring out a new hymnal. A committee consisting of James White, J. N. Andrews, Uriah Smith, and others was set up to gather hymns for the new book "free from the prevailing errors of the age." They wanted to make certain that none of the pieces contained doctrinal heresy, since "most hymns sustain one or more of the popular 'fables' of our times."

As with other hymns set to secular tunes, the choice of Stephen Foster's tune OLD FOLKS AT HOME for "Land of Light" made singing it easy. This was especially helpful, since generally Adventist audiences then had neither notes in their hymnals nor musical instruments to accompany them when singing.

Land of Light

OLD FOLKS AT HOME
Stephen Foster (1826-1864)
Uriah Smith, 1856 (1832-1903)
Arr. by Sandra G. Gray, 1988

1. Up to a land of light we're go-ing, Joys, joys are there;
2. No earth-ly charm may then al-lure us, Or lead a-stray;
3. Then let no toil-ing heart grow wea-ry, Or faint-ing be;

Where pain and sor-row no more know-ing, We shall its glo-ries share.
Since all its fad-ed hopes as-sure us, They too shall van-ish a-way.
Soon we'll for-get our ex-ile drea-ry, Joy-ous in vic-to-ry.

Soon shall we hail the ra-diant dawn-ing Of end-less day,
In heav-en on-ly can our trea-sure Be laid se-cure;
There where our heart's af-fec-tion cen-ter, A-round the throne;

E'en now the light of that glad morn-ing, Breaks o'er the shad-owy way.
There on-ly may we seek for plea-sure, Holy, im-mor-tal and pure.
Those pearl-y man-sions soon we'll en-ter, And be for-e'er at home.

Refrain

There be-side Life's flow-ing riv-er, And Life's fade-less tree,

We shall in-her-it joys for-ev-er, Joys that are bound-less and free.

LET OTHERS SEEK
A HOME BELOW

The first Seventh-day Adventist hymnal to include this hymn was the one compiled by James White in 1861. It continued to be reprinted in various Adventist hymnals through the 1941 *Church Hymnal.*

The words of the hymn are from the last two stanzas of a five-stanza poem written by William Hunter, D.D. (1811-1877). He came to the United States at the age of 6; eventually he joined the Methodist Church.

The three stanzas not picked up by our Adventist pioneers are:

1. My heavenly home is bright and fair:
   No pain nor death can enter there;
   Its glittering towers the sun outshine;
   That heavenly mansion shall be mine.

Refrain: I'm going home, I'm going home,
   I'm going home to die no more.
   To die no more, to die no more,
   I'm going home to die no more.

2. My Father's house is built on high,
   Far, far above the starry sky.
   When from this earthly prison free,
   That heavenly mansion mine shall be.

3. While here, a stranger far from home,
   Affliction's waves may round me foam;
   Although, like Lazarus, sick and poor,
   My heavenly mansion is secure.

James White used only the fourth and fifth stanzas from the original poem. He divided each stanza in half, added the phrase "We'll be gathered home," and then set the words to a different tune. In addition, White also changed "o'erflow" to "o'erthrow" in the second line of his first stanza, and replaced "All nature sink and cease to be" with "That heavenly mansion stands for me," to close the fifth stanza.

The tune LAND OF REST was composed by Dr. William Miller (1801-1878) and arranged in 1859 by William James Kirkpatrick (1838-1921).

In addition to the overall sentiment of the hymn that doubtless appealed to both James White and the other pioneers, the third stanza with its references to the falling of the stars (1833) and the Dark Day (1780) held special meaning for those who were looking for the soon return of Jesus. While here on earth, Christ had predicted, "The sun shall be darkened, and the moon shall not give her light, and the stars of heaven shall fall" (Mark 13:24, 25).

According to eyewitness accounts, on May 19, 1780, all across New England the sun did precisely as Christ had predicted.

"Friday morning early the Sun appeared red, as it had done for several days before, the wind about south-west, a light breeze, and the clouds from the south-west came over between eight and nine o'clock, the Sun was quite shut in, and it began to shower . . . , and it rained but little. About eleven o'clock the darkness was such as to demand our attention, and put us upon making observations. At half past eleven, in a room with three windows, 24 panes each, all open towards the south-east and south, large print could not be read by persons of good eyes. About twelve o'clock the windows still open, a candle cast a shade so well defined on the wall as that profiles were taken with as much ease as they could have been in the night. About one o'clock a glint of light which had continued 'till this time in the east, shut in, and the darkness was greater than it had been for any time before. Between one and two o'clock, the wind from the west freshened a little, and a glint appeared in that quarter. We dined about two . . . [with] two candles burning on the table. In the time of the greatest darkness some of the dunghill fowls went to their roost: Cocks crowed in answer to one another as they commonly do in the night: Woodcocks which are night birds, whistled as they do *only* in the dark: Frogs peeped—In short, there was the appearance of midnight at noonday" (letter dated May 22, 1780, printed in *The Boston Gazette and the Country Journal*, May 29, 1780, p. 4).

The Connecticut legislature was meeting in Hartford, May 19, 1780. It is reported that the unexpected darkness elicited a most interesting response from the legislators:

"A very general opinion prevailed, that the day of judgment was

103

at hand. The House of Representatives, being unable to transact their business, adjourned. A proposal to adjourn the Council was under consideration. When the opinion of Colonel [Abraham] Davenport was asked, he answered, 'I am against an adjournment. The day of judgment is either approaching, or it is not. If it is not, there is no cause for an adjournment: if it is, I choose to be found doing my duty. I wish therefore that candles . . . be brought" (Dwight Timothy, quoted in *Connecticut Historical Collection*, 1836, p. 403).

Although most authorities acknowledge that natural causes, probably a forest fire, caused the Dark Day in 1780, Adventists have long held that it is the *fact*, not the *cause*, of the darkness that is significant. This is also true of the other sign that Christ foretold would occur before His return—the falling of the stars.

An eyewitness describes what happened on the night of November 12, 13, 1833:

"Between five and six o'clock on Wednesday morning, November 13, we observed one of the most beautiful phenomena we remember ever to have seen. Upon looking out at the window a great number of what are called *shooting stars* appeared radiating from different parts of the heavens. We noticed that they shot in every direction, except upward, from common centres. These centres appeared to be, to speak in common language, about two or three hundred yards apart, covering the whole expanse, and the radiations were not very rapid, leaving a streak of mild light on the unsullied blue. Just before the meteors became extinct their velocities were lessened, and they seemed gradually to expire as they ceased to move, very much like rockets after their explosion in the heavens.

"While we were gazing on this most beautiful of all celestial phenomena that we ever witnessed, our milk-man drove up to the door, and stated that he had been astonished for an hour at the millions of stars which were darting all over the face of the heavens. A female friend who lodged in a room opening to the east had been attracted to the window by the light glaring in, and stated, for half an hour before we noticed the phenomenon, she had been wrapped in wonder and delight at the mild sublimity and glory of the millions of lines of light which were gradually appearing and disappearing in succession.

"[In viewing the phenomenon] . . . the first impression made on our minds was that of groups of sportive invisible beings concealed in the heavens, and from behind the blue curtain of the sky, letting off in all directions from themselves, rockets of pure electricity, peculiarly tempered to produce a steady gentle motion, followed by a mild and soothing light. And what added to the impressiveness of the scene was the profound silence amid the innumerable movements" (*Christian Advocate and Journal*, Nov. 22, 1833).

From time to time James White referred to both the Dark Day and the falling of the stars as fulfillment of the signs preceding Christ's returning. In fact, during 1862, the very next year after White included, in the 1861 hymnal, "Let Others Seek a Home Below," with its references to these two phenomena, he published two tracts, both of which devote several pages to a discussion of these two signs: *Brief Exposition of Matthew Twenty-Four* and a new *The Signs of the Times, Showing That the Second Coming of Christ Is at the Doors*. Clearly, when the early Adventists sang this hymn, including its third stanza with its references to these two signs of Christ's approaching return, the words meant a great deal to them.

Let Others Seek a Home Below

LAND OF REST

Anon.

Dr. William Miller

1. Let oth-ers seek a home be-low,
2. Be mine the hap-pier lot to own,
3. Then, fail this earth, let stars de-cline.
4. Though des-o-la-tion here may be,

We'll be gath-ered home;

Which flames de-vour or waves o'er-throw,
A heaven-ly man-sion near the throne.
And sun and moon re-fuse to shine,
That heaven-ly man-sion stands for me,

We'll be gath-ered home.

Refrain

We'll work till Je-sus comes, We'll work till Je-sus comes,
We'll work   We'll work

We'll work till Je-sus comes, And we'll be gath-ered home.
We'll work

LO! AN ANGEL LOUD PROCLAIMING

Lo! An Angel Loud Proclaiming" appears to be the first hymn written by a Sabbathkeeping Adventist as well as the first printed in a Sabbathkeeping Adventist publication, though not the first written in the Seventh-day Adventist tradition. Joseph Bates printed this hymn in his small book called *A Vindication of the Seventh-day Sabbath, and the Commandments of God: With a Further History of God's Peculiar People From 1847 to 1848.* The preface to that work is dated January 1848, Fairhaven, Massachusetts. The book was actually printed across the river from Fairhaven, in New Bedford, at the press of Henry Oliphant, the same printer that Bates had used to print his first Sabbath tract in 1846.

Instructions printed with the hymn indicate that it is to be sung to the tune ZION. James White included the hymn in his 1849 hymnal, where it was entitled "Second Advent History." In the 1852 hymnal he called it "The Three Messages," the title that it carried through to the 1861 hymnal. The song was then dropped until *Hymns and Tunes* came out in 1886, where it was once again included, though with slightly altered words. The four stanzas as revised in 1886 are the ones used in *Early Advent Singing*. Gurney's original stanzas are as follows (since his original fourth stanza was not changed in 1886, it is not repeated here):

1. Lo! An angel *loud* proclaiming,
    With the gospel of good news,
  To every kindred, tongue, and people:
    Fear the Lord; give glory due;
  Proclamation
    Of the hour of judgment near.

2. Lo! Another angel follows,
    With another solemn cry!
  Babylon the *great* is fallen
    Peals like thunder through the sky:
  Let "thy people,"

Now forsake her POIS'NOUS CREEDS.

3. Yet, a third and solemn message,
　　Now proclaims a *final doom*;
Who "worship *Beast* or *Image*"
　　Soon shall drink the wrath of God:
Without mixture,
　　Mercy *now* no longer pleads.

5. Hear a voice from Heav'n proclaiming,
　　"Write" the message, "firm decree,"
Bless'd are they who die in Jesus,
　　"From *henceforth*" for ever be:
The Spirit sanctions,
　　And the Saints ADORE HIS LAW.

The words were written by Heman S. Gurney, a blacksmith friend of Joseph Bates. They refer to the Advent experience at the time. The early Sabbathkeepers viewed the Millerites as having proclaimed the messages of the first two angels of Revelation 14. In James White's view, the proclamation of the Second Advent gospel by the Millerites was the first angel's message. When the churches expelled the Millerites from their membership, White viewed that as the second angel's message—coming out of Babylon.

The first to link the mark of the beast in the third angel's message to the fourth-commandment Sabbath truth was Joseph Bates, in 1847. It is therefore likely from the wording that this hymn was written by Gurney sometime in 1847—after Bates had linked the Sabbath with the mark of the beast.

H. S. Gurney, who lived near Bates in Fairhaven, came to be called the "singing blacksmith" because he enjoyed singing at his forge to the accompaniment of hammer and anvil. He was a brawny man, about six feet tall, who became a Millerite Adventist. In early 1844 he accompanied Bates on a preaching itinerary through northern Maryland. (See the hymn "I'm a Pilgrim" for an incident that happened on that trip.)

After the disappointment of October 22, 1844, Bates and Gurney remained friends. When Bates accepted the Sabbath and wrote his first small tract on that topic in 1846, it was Gurney who finished paying off the bill. Bates had arranged to have the pamphlet printed with the understanding that he would pay the printer as rapidly as he could. When he went to Benjamin Lindsey, the printer, to make the last payment, he found that it had already been paid. Gurney had unexpectedly received payment of $100 owed him by his employer, who had refused to pay him when he went on the preaching trip to Maryland with Joseph Bates in 1844. Gurney now decided to apply the money to the final payment of Bates's Sabbath tract. The printer professed to Bates that he did not know who had paid it, so Bates considered it another of God's mysterious providences and never found out.

About 1845, Gurney heard Ellen Harmon (later White) relate one of her visions at a meeting in New Bedford, Massachusetts. Though he found no fault with what she said, he still wanted to check into her experience before accepting her gift as genuine. So he traveled up to Portland, Maine, to investigate for himself. He talked to her friends and acquaintances, including her father, Robert Harmon, to determine just what type of person she was. After determining that her Christian experience matched the spiritual gift that she had been given, he accepted her visions as genuine. In fact, he paid half the expense of printing her first vision in a broadside, or poster. Dated April 6, 1846, it was her first publication.

Gurney attended some of the Sabbath conferences in 1848 and later moved to Michigan, where he continued his blacksmithing. He died in 1896.

Although "Lo! An Angel Loud Proclaiming" has been entirely overlooked when pioneer songs are now used, it does maintain the distinction of being the first hymn written and published by a Sabbathkeeping Adventist.

Lo! An Angel Loud Proclaiming

ZION

Heman S. Gurney, 1847 (1817-1896)　　　　　*Thomas Hastings, 1830 (1784-1872)*

1. Lo! an an - gel loud pro - claim - ing, Brings the gos - pel of good cheer;
2. Lo! an - oth - er an - gel fol - lows, With an - oth - er so - lemn cry
3. Yet, a third and so-lemn mes - sage Now a fin - al doom pro - claims
4. Here are they who now are wait - ing, And have pa-tience to en - dure;

Ev - ery kin - dred, tongue, and peo - ple, Fear the Lord soon to ap - pear!
"Ba - by - lon the great is fal - len!" Peals like thun-der thro' the sky;
All who wor - ship beast or im - age Soon shall feel the a-veng - ing flames:
While the dra - gon's hosts are rag - ing, These con - fide in God, se - cure:

Pro - cla - ma - tion Of the hour of judg - ment near.
"Let my peo - ple Now from all her er - ors fly."
Grace no long - er Shel - ters their un - wor - thy names.
Faith of Je - sus And com -mand -ments keep them pure.

Pro - cla - ma - tion Of the hour of judg - ment near.
"Let my peo - ple Now from all her er - ors fly."
Grace no long - er Shel - ters their un - wor - thy names.
Faith of Je - sus And com - mand-ments keep them pure.

LONG UPON THE MOUNTAINS

nnie R. Smith, the most prolific of the early Sabbathkeeping hymn writers, was the author of this hymn. The piece was Annie's second contribution to the *Advent Review and Sabbath Herald*. (For the story of Annie Smith, see under "How Far From Home?") The first poem that she wrote after becoming a Sabbathkeeper, entitled "Fear Not, Little Flock," was printed in the September 16, 1851, issue. Immediately, James White invited Annie to come to Saratoga Springs, New York, where he and Ellen were living at the time, to help publish the paper. At first she declined, though a short time later she went. It is quite likely that "Long Upon the Mountains" was her first contribution to the paper after she arrived in Saratoga Springs.

Although no indication is given as to where she was when she wrote the poem, her next poem, which was published just two weeks later in the following issue of the *Review and Herald*, says "Saratoga Springs" at the bottom of it. Most certainly Annie had arrived there at least by then to help James White.

Before the name "Seventh-day Adventist" was chosen in 1860, the early Sabbathkeepers used expressions such as "the remnant" and "the scattered flock" to refer to themselves. In fact, Ellen Harmon's (later White) first broadside was entitled "To the Little Remnant Scattered Abroad." It was printed on April 6, 1846. So Annie Smith's poem about the "Scattered Flock" with its references to commandment keeping and the Second Coming would have been very understandable to the few Sabbathkeepers then in existence.

There must have been quite an air of excitement in the west end of Battle Creek, Michigan, on May 20, 1863. Twenty delegates, representing six of the seven conferences then in existence (Iowa, Michigan, Minnesota, Ohio, New York, and Wisconsin; only Vermont sent no delegates), plus many individuals crowded into the small Adventist meetinghouse. Measuring just 28 by 42 feet, the building had been erected in 1857 at a cost of $881.39. It was our second church in Battle Creek. All knew why they were there that evening; they were responding to the notices in the *Review and Herald* calling them together to form the General Conference of Seventh-day Adventists.

History does not record who announced the opening hymn at

that first session of the General Conference, but the title of the hymn is recorded. As they all joined in singing the first stanza of Annie Smith's hymn, doubtless it took on a new and special meaning to those gathered there on that historic occasion.

> Long upon the mountains weary,
>   Have the scattered flock been torn;
> Dark the desert paths, and dreary,
>   Grievous trials have they borne.
> Now the gathering call is sounding,
>   Solemn in its waning voice;
> Union, faith, and love abounding,
>   Bid the little flock rejoice.

As they met the following day, May 21, and adopted a constitution for their new General Conference of Seventh-day Adventists, "union, faith, and love abounding," certainly did "bid the little flock rejoice."

Reporting on that first session, Uriah Smith wrote:

"The majority of those present from any considerable distance were the delegates from the different churches in this State, and from abroad, and were consequently those whose hearts were all aglow with love for the glorious present truth. Their happy and hopeful countenances, and cordial greetings, as they arrived from their various, and in many instances far distant, localities, are among the pleasant scenes which it is not for the pen to attempt to portray. . . .

"The influence of this meeting cannot fail to be good. We are certain that those who were present, as they look back upon the occasion, will not be able to discover an unpleasant feature. And as they separated to go to their homes, courage and good cheer seemed to be the unanimous feelings" (*Review and Herald*, May 26, 1863).

"Long Upon the Mountains" was first published in the *Review and Herald*, December 9, 1851, along with the text Ezekiel 34:12: "So will I seek out my sheep, and will deliver them out of all places where they have been scattered in the cloudy and dark day."

In the original printing of the poem, there is no indication that it was intended as a hymn, nor is the piece even given a title. However, the following year James White included it in his 1852 hymnal called *Hymns for Second Advent Believers*. There it was called "The Scattered Flock." In Annie Smith's own little book of poems, which

112

she edited but which was printed shortly after her death in 1855, she included it in her section of hymns. It has continued to be retained in the main Seventh-day Adventist hymnals since that time.

Long Upon the Mountains

Eze. 34:12
Annie R. Smith, 1851 (1828-1855)

GREENVILLE
Jean J. Rousseau, 1752 (1712-1778)

1. Long up-on the moun-tains wea - ry, Have the scat-tered flock been torn;
2. Now the light of truth they're seek -ing, In its on-ward track pur - sue;
3. In that light of light and beau-ty, In that gold-en cit - y fair,
4. Soon He comes! with clouds de-scend-ing; All His saints, en -tombed a - rise;

Dark the des - sert paths, and drea - ry; Griev-ous tri - als have they borne.
All the ten com-mand-ments keep -ing, They are ho - ly, just, and true.
Soon its pear - ly gates they'll en - ter, And of all its glo - ries share.
The re -deemed in an -thems blend - ing, Shout their vic - t'ry thro' the skies.

Now the gath-ering call is sound - ing, Sol-emn in its warn - ing voice;
On the words of life they're feed - ing, Pre-cious to their taste so sweet;
There, di - vine the soul's ex - pan - sions; Free from sin, and death, and pain;
O, we long for Thine ap - pear - ing; Come, O Sav - ior, quick - ly come!

Un - ion, faith, and love a -bound-ing, Bid the lit - tle flock re - joice.
All their Mas - ter's pre-cepts heed - ing, Bow-ing hum -bly at His feet.
Tears will nev - er dim those man - sions Where the saints im - mor - tal reign.
Bless - ed hope, our spir - its cheer - ing, Take Thy ran-somed chil - dren home.

LORD, IN THE MORNING

The first home actually owned by James and Ellen White still stands on Wood Street in Battle Creek, Michigan. It is currently owned by Adventist Heritage Ministry, and is available for tours by visitors who wish to see it.

In 1855 the Whites moved from Rochester, New York, to Battle Creek. Upon their arrival, they rented a house for $1.50 per week. James White was making about $4 per week at the time, at the Review office. Later, Cyrenius Smith, one of five Adventists who originally invited the Whites to move to Battle Creek, sold two village lots totaling nearly an acre and a half to James White on August 4, 1856, for $230.* Friends of the Whites assisted with the purchase.

The lots were covered with trees and are described as being "situated in the extreme western part of Battle Creek." Again, with the assistance of friends—a few contributing money, but most giving labor—the Whites soon erected a moderate-sized cottage house at a cost of about $500.

The same kindhearted friends also helped clear the land, except for a little grove of second-growth oak in the northeast corner. At James White's request, this was left as a place for retreat and prayer. Some of the land was also converted into a flower garden. The Whites lived here until April 15, 1863, when the house was sold for $1,480, and they moved elsewhere in Battle Creek.

Nearly 75 years later, William C. White, third son of James and Ellen White, recalled what the daily schedule was like while growing up in the White family:

"With but little variation, the daily program of the White family was something like this: At six o'clock all were up. Often Mother had been writing for two or three hours, and the cook had been busy in the kitchen since five o'clock. By six-thirty breakfast was ready. . . . At the breakfast table [Mother] . . . sometimes . . . would relate to the family some interesting portions of what she had written. Father would sometimes tell us of the work in which he was engaged, or relate interesting incidents regarding the progress of the cause, east and west.

"At seven o'clock all assembled in the parlor for morning worship. Father would read an appropriate scripture, with comments, and then lead in the morning song of praise or supplication, in which all joined. The most frequent was:

> " 'Lord, in the morning Thou shalt hear
>   My voice ascending high;
> To Thee will I direct my prayer,
> To Thee lift up mine eye.'

"This or some other song of a somewhat similar character was sung with hearty vigor, and then Father prayed. He did not 'offer a prayer'; he *prayed* with earnestness and with solemn reverence. He pleaded for those blessings most needed by himself and his family, and for the prosperity of the cause of God. . . .

"When father was away from home, Mother conducted the family worship. If both were gone, the one in charge of the home led out. The worship hour was as regularly observed as the hours for breakfast and dinner.

"After breakfast, Father left promptly for his work in the Review office, except when detained by Mother, with a request that he listen to what she had been writing.

"After Father had left the house, Mother enjoyed spending half an hour in her flower garden during those portions of the year when flowers could be cultivated. In this her children were encouraged to work with her. Then she would devote three or four hours to her writing. Her afternoons were usually occupied with a variety of activities—sewing, mending, knitting, darning, and working in her flower garden, with occasional shopping trips to town or visits to the sick.

"If there was no evening meeting, between seven and eight o'clock or later, the whole family would assemble again for worship. If the day's work permitted us to be called to prayers early, we listened to Mother as she read some instructive article from religious papers or books. Then Father, if present, read a chapter from the Bible and prayed, thanking God for the blessings of the day, and committing the family to God's care for the night" (*Review and Herald*, Feb. 13, 1936, pp. 6, 7).

The hymn "Lord, in the Morning" continued to be a favorite as Ellen White's grandchildren were growing up. Granddaughter Ella (White) Robinson recalled ". . . waking up with, 'Lord, in the morning Thou shalt hear my voice ascending high,' and going to sleep with, 'Sweet hour of prayer.' " "No wonder," she commented, "that both these hymns were among Grandma's favorites."

"Lord, in the Morning" was also sung at the start of an historic day in Adventist history. Meeting at sunrise in our second little church in Battle Creek, Michigan, on October 1, 1860, the order of business was to adopt a constitution for the publishing association. Once accomplished, the meeting was adjourned, only to reconvene later that same day to decide upon a name for the new organization. After considerable discussion "Seventh-day Adventist" was chosen. It was then overwhelmingly voted to recommend that the name also be used by our churches. At the time, we had no conference organizations, but at least we now had a name.

"Lord, in the Morning" was introduced into Seventh-day Adventist hymnody in James White's second hymnal, *Hymns for Second Advent Believers*, published in 1852.

---

* Arthur L. White seems to be incorrect when he states that the two lots cost $25 each (*Ellen G. White, The Early Years*, p. 334). The deed (Calhoun Co., Mich., Deeds Lib. 40, p. 434) states that lots 64 and 65 of Manchesters Addition to Battle Creek cost $230.

Lord, in the Morning

MEAR

Isaac Watts, 1719 (1674-1748)   *Aaron Williams (1731-1776)*

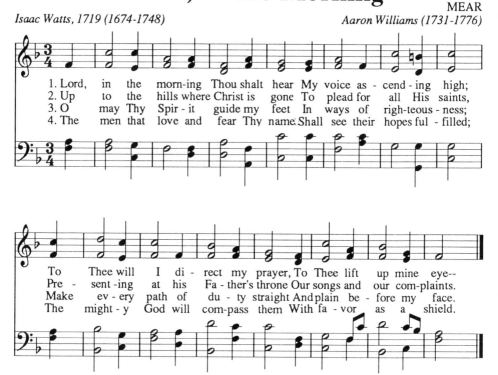

1. Lord, in the morn-ing Thou shalt hear My voice as - cend - ing high;
2. Up to the hills where Christ is gone To plead for all His saints,
3. O may Thy Spir - it guide my feet In ways of righ-teous - ness;
4. The men that love and fear Thy name Shall see their hopes ful - filled;

To Thee will I di - rect my prayer, To Thee lift up mine eye--
Pre - sent -ing at his Fa - ther's throne Our songs and our com-plaints.
Make ev - ery path of du - ty straight And plain be - fore my face.
The might - y God will com-pass them With fa - vor as a shield.

O BROTHER, BE FAITHFUL

The early Sabbathkeepers faced a real problem with their singing. Their earliest hymnals contained no music, just the words. In addition, it may be recalled that they used no musical instruments in their worship services. Further, their few members were scattered all over the northeastern United States. Often they could meet with other Sabbathkeepers only once or twice a year, when a visiting minister passed through.

In the meantime, they tried to recall the tunes to the hymns they had learned at their previous meeting. If they did not happen to remember a tune correctly, and others did not either, one can imagine what the singing must have sounded like by the time of the next meeting several months later!

Joseph Clarke, a prominent layman at the time, wrote a letter to *The Advent Review and Sabbath Herald* that was published in the November 10, 1859, issue. He described the situation at a recent meeting he had attended:

"I lately attended a conference where brethren and sisters from different sections were gathered; and it was good to see them there. . . . But alas! when we sang, one prolonged a quarter note until it consumed the time of a whole note, with a hold and swell besides. Some were singing one verse, until others had progressed pretty well into the next; and the ending word of each verse echoed and re-echoed, each according to the different notions of propriety, which each locality administered for itself. . . . It would be too much to suppose that different voices, from different places, with different styles of singing, should sing in perfect harmony; but certainly, it might be very much improved!"

One partial solution to the problem was to write religious words and put them to secular tunes of the day. In a time when secular and religious society were not as far apart as they now are, this was a viable option. When the scattered believers came together after being apart for some length of time, they could still sing pretty much in unison because the words were printed in the hymnals and they were familiar with the tunes.

The 1855 hymnal was the first to contain any music notes. Subsequent hymnals each contained more, although it was not until 1878, when James Edson White, the second son of James and Ellen

119

White, published his *Song Anchor*, that a Seventh-day Adventist hymnal had music for each song it contained.

Uriah Smith (1832-1903) wrote the hymn "O Brother, Be Faithful," which was first published in the September 27, 1853, issue of the *Review and Herald*. Instructions printed with it listed the tune as "Be Kind to the Loved Ones at Home." That tune had been written by Isaac Baker Woodbury. The original secular words, given below, were written in 1847 by Jacob E. Hosmer.

Be Kind to the Loved Ones at Home

1. Be kind to thy father, for when thou wert young,
    Who loved thee so fondly as he?
  He caught the first accents that fell from thy tongue,
    And joined in thy innocent glee.
  Be kind to thy father, for now he is old,
    His locks intermingled with gray;
  His footsteps are feeble, once fearless and bold,
    Thy father is passing away.

2. Be kind to thy mother, for lo! on her brow
    May traces of sorrow be seen;
  Oh, well may'st thou cherish and comfort her now,
    For loving and kind hath she been.
  Remember thy mother, for thee will she pray
    As long as God giveth her breath;
  With accents of kindness then cheer her lone way,
    E'en to the dark valley of death.

3. Be kind to thy brother, his heart will have dearth,
    If the smile of thy joy be withdrawn;
  The flowers of feeling will fade at their birth,
    If the dew of affection be gone.
  Be kind to thy brother wherever you are,
    The love of a brother shall be
  An ornament purer and richer by far
    Than pearls from the depth of the sea.

4. Be kind to thy sister, not many may know
     The depth of true sisterly love;
 The wealth of the ocean lies fathoms below
     The surface that sparkles above.
 Be kind to thy father, once fearless and bold,
     Be kind to thy mother so near;
 Be kind to thy brother, nor show thy heart cold,
     Be kind to thy sister so dear.

The first hymnal that "O Brother, Be Faithful" was printed in was the *Supplement* to the 1852 hymnal, published in 1853. This hymn has continued to be retained in all major Seventh-day Adventist hymnals since that time.

O Brother, Be Faithful

FAITHFUL

Uriah Smith, 1853 (1832-1903)

Isaac Woodbury, 1847 (1819-1858)

1. O broth - er, be faith - ful! soon Je - sus will come,
2. O broth - er, be faith - ful! the cit - ty of gold,
3. O broth - er, be faith - ful! He soon will de - scend,
4. O broth - er, be faith - ful! e - ter - ni - ty's years

For whom we have wait - ed so long; O, soon we shall en - ter our
Pre - pared for the good and the blest, Is wait - ing its por - tals of
Cre - a - tions's om - ni - po-tent King, While le - gions of an - gels His
Shall tell for thy faith - ful-ness now, When bright smiles of glad-ness shall

glo - ri - ous home, And join in the con - quer - ror's song.
pearl to un - fold, And wel - come thee in - to thy rest.
char - iot at - tend, And palm wreaths, of vic - to - ry bring.
scat - ter thy tears, A cor - o - net gleam on thy brow.

O broth - er, be faith - ful! for why should we prove
Then, broth - er, be faith - ful! not long shall we stay
O broth - er, be faith - ful! and soon shalt thou hear
O broth - er, be faith - ful! the prom - ise is sure,

Un - faith - ful to Him who hath shown Such deep, such un-bound -
In wea - ry-ness here, and for - lorn, Time's dark night of sor -
Thy Sav - ior pro-nounce the glad word, Well done, faith-ful ser -
That waits for the faith - ful and tried; To reign with the ran -

ed and in - fi - nite love-- Who died to re - deem us His own.
row is wear - ing a - way, We haste to the glo - ri - ous morn.
ant, thy ti - tle is clear, To en - ter the joy of thy Lord.
somed, im - mor - tal and pure, And ev - er with Je - sus a - bide.

ROCK OF AGES

J ames White first included this hymn in his 1861 *Hymns for Those Who Keep the Commandments of God and the Faith of Jesus*. Only two stanzas were included, and it was set to the same tune still used today. Through the years Ellen White referred occasionally to this hymn in her writings, sometimes even quoting a few lines from it.

At the 1903 General Conference session held March 27-April 13, in the Oakland, California, Seventh-day Adventist Church, Ellen White spoke a number of times. Several important issues were being considered by those in attendance. Among the most divisive were ownership and control of the Battle Creek Sanitarium, and whether or not the General Conference delegates should elect the president directly. Ever since the 1901 reorganization, the General Conference Committee had elected a chairman who served at their pleasure. During the intervening two years, this arrangement had already proven unsatisfactory.

Also, in light of the disastrous fires in Battle Creek in 1902, which saw the burning of both the Battle Creek Sanitarium and the Review and Herald Publishing Company, another issue being discussed was whether to move the General Conference headquarters from Battle Creek "to some place favorable for its work in the Atlantic states."

In her talks, Ellen White spoke to the issues. After referring to the disastrous fires of 1902, she urged that a reformation take place in our institutions. She urged unity with Dr. John Harvey Kellogg, and spoke of her long years of support of the Battle Creek Sanitarium. But she also warned against the "spurious scientific theories" (pantheism) that were being taught the medical students there. As to the possible move of the General Conference, she approved of it, saying that she did not know where they should move to. "But this I will say, Never lay a stone or brick in Battle Creek to rebuild the Review office there. God has a better place for it."

Considering the strong feelings held by some of the delegates, it is perhaps understandable that in both her Tuesday and Wednesday, March 31 and April 1, devotionals, and again in her Sabbath sermon on April 4, Ellen White spoke about faultfinding, criticism, and backbiting. That she felt strongly about her Sabbath message needing to be heard by the delegates is obvious because she spoke for about an hour and a quarter, in spite of having a bad cold.

In part, Ellen White said during her sermon:

"When you are tempted to speak cross words, pray for grace to resist the temptation. Remember that your children will speak as they hear you speak. By your example you are educating them. Remember that if you speak cross words to fellow church members, you would speak the same kind of words in heaven, were you permitted to enter there. But you never will be unless you change.

"This is our washing and ironing time—the time when we are to cleanse our robes of character in the blood of the Lamb. . . .

"There are churches in which the spirituality has been almost killed, because the spirit of backbiting has been allowed to enter. . . . My brethren, you will never enter heaven with a spirit of faultfinding. I ask you to get rid of this spirit before you leave this meeting. Do not take it back with you to your home churches. . . .

"When the mercy and love of God are cherished in our hearts, we shall not manifest a cold, hard spirit in the home and in the church toward those who do not agree with us in every idea that we hold. We all believe that the Word of God is true. Then let us, by a careful study of this Word, find out how to remove the differences existing among us. God will speak to us through His Word, and will reveal His salvation to us.

"May God help us not to be a disturbance in His church. He has never commanded us to carry on a disturbing work. Brethren, I beseech you not to leave Oakland to go to your home churches until you can leave behind all your hard-heartedness, all your complaining, all your criticism. These act as the leaven of evil. One man in an institution with an unamiable spirit causes contention that leaves the whole institution with the same spirit. It is God's desire that in all our institutions there shall be perfect harmony and agreement, that from them the light of heaven may be reflected. Open the windows of the soul heavenward and close them earthward, that the bright rays of the glory of God may shine into your hearts" (General Conference Bulletin, 1903, pp. 89, 90).

At the end of her sermon, Ellen White invited those in the congregation who recognized they had erred and who wanted to overcome through the Lord's power to stand. All rose. While they were standing, "Sister White then offered a most earnest prayer." After completing it, she invited the congregation to sing "Rock of Ages."

A few days later, in writing to friends about the previous Sabbath's service, Ellen White recalled, "Some who for 40 years have frequently heard me speak said they had never before heard me give so powerful a discourse. No one could doubt that the power of God rested upon me."

After describing the call she made for people to stand, she continued her account of what happened.

"Then we knelt, and as my soul was drawn out in earnest prayer the congregation realized that the power of God was upon me. I had much reason to be thankful that the Lord so evidently sustained me. I asked the congregation to sing 'Rock of ages, cleft for me, let me hide myself in Thee.' This hymn was a prayer to God in which all could join, and I know that angels of God united with the petition that rose from so many hearts and voices" (*Ellen G. White Manuscript Releases*, vol. 17, p. 290).

"Rock of Ages" was written in 1776 by Augustus Montague Toplady (1740-1778) while he was living in London, England. The tune TOPLADY was written in 1830 by Thomas Hastings (1784-1872) of New York to commemorate the author of the hymn's words.

Rock of Ages

Augustus M. Toplady, 1776 (1740-1778) alt.

TOPLADY

Thomas Hastings, 1830 (1784-1872)

1. Rock of A - ges, cleft for me, Let me hide my-self in Thee;
2. Not the la - bors of my hands Can ful - fill Thy law's demands;
3. When my pil - grim - age I close, Vic - tor o'er the last of foes,

Let the wa - ter and the blood, From Thy riv - en side which flowed,
Could my zeal no re-spite know, Could my tears for - ev - er flow,
When I soar to worlds un-known, And be - hold Thee on Thy throne,

Be of sin the dou-ble cure, Cleanse me from its guilt and power.
All for sin could not a - tone; Thou must save, and Thou a - lone.
Rock of A - ges, cleft for me, Let me hide my -self in Thee.

SAFELY THROUGH
ANOTHER WEEK

The Sabbath was one distinctive doctrine that James White especially felt needed to be featured in the early hymnals he compiled. His 1849 collection, *Hymns for God's Peculiar People That Keep the Commandments of God and the Faith of Jesus,* contained three songs that have the word "Sabbath" in their titles and two more that refer to the day. His second hymnal, published in 1852, was actually called *Hymns for Second Advent Believers Who Observe the Sabbath of the Lord.* One section, entitled "Sabbath Hymns," contained 16 songs on the topic.

"Safely Through Another Week" was written in 1774 by John Newton (1725-1807). Originally entitled "Saturday Evening," which was when the Sabbath began according to Newton's belief, the hymn had five stanzas when written. Since the hymn's first appearance in Adventist hymnody in the 1861 hymnal, only four of its stanzas have been included in our hymnals. The tune SABBATH was composed in 1824 by Lowell Mason (1792-1872).

Ever since the Sabbath's introduction among Seventh-day Adventists, it has been the high point of the week for those who keep it. Joseph Bates, sometimes called "the apostle of the Sabbath" because he wrote our first Sabbath tract, used to exclaim: "Oh, how I do love this Sabbath!"

The same feeling of excitement was felt by countless other early Adventists, including the family of James and Ellen White. Of all the days of the week, the hours of the Sabbath were recalled most fondly in the memories of Ellen White's grandchildren.

During the last 15 years of her life, Mrs. White lived at her Elmshaven home in northern California. Nearby lived her third son, William C. White, and his family. With all the activities of the week keeping everyone busy, the special hours of the Sabbath were eagerly looked forward to, even by the youngest members of the family. Lamp chimneys were cleaned, food was prepared, shoes were shined, baths were taken, and bouquets of flowers were arranged, all in anticipation of the Sabbath. And nobody wanted to miss sundown worship on Friday evening at Grandma White's house. The whole family assembled together there to welcome in the Sabbath.

Eagerly, everyone gathered in the large parlor, waiting for Mrs. White to join them. Soon they heard footsteps coming down the stairs. Mrs. White came in and seated herself in a comfortable rocking chair next to the fireplace. Hymnbooks were passed out and all joined in singing the hymns that were chosen by various ones.

The familiar sounds of the pump organ accompanied by the voices of the eager singers reminded everyone that the special hours of the Sabbath had begun. Another 24 hours of warm fellowship with each other and communion with God was underway. Later Mrs. White would read a passage of Scripture, after which all would pray, not long prayers, just short ones so that everyone had a chance to participate. No wonder the Sabbath stood out in the memories of Ellen White's grandchildren. For them, it really was the highlight of their week.

Safely Through Another Week

SABBATH

John Newton, 1774; alt. (1725-1807)   *Lowell Mason, 1824 (1792-1872)*

1. Safe - ly through an -oth- er week   God has brought   us   on   our   way;
2. While we seek sup-plies of grace   Through the dear   Re - deem-er's   name,
3. When the morn shall bid us   rise,   May we feel   Thy pres-ence   near,
4. May the gos - pel's joy-ful sound   Con-quer sin - ners, com-fort   saints;

Let us   now   a bless ing   seek,   Wait - ing   in His courts to - day;
Show Thy   re - con - cil - ing   face,   Take a - way our sin   and   shame;
May Thy   glo - ry meet our   eyes   When we   in Thy house ap - pear;
Make the   fruits   of grace a - bound,   Bring re - lief to all   com - plaints;

Day of   all   the week the best,   Em - blem   of   e - ter - nal   rest;
From our   world - ly cares set   free   May we   rest   this day in   Thee.
Here af - ford   us, Lord, a   taste   Of   our   ev - er - last-ing   feast.
Thus may   all   our Sab-baths   be   Till we   rise   to reign with   Thee.

Day of   all   the week the best,   Emblem   of   e - ter - nal   rest.
From our   world - ly cares set   free   May we   rest this   day   in   Thee.
Here af - ford   us, Lord, a   taste   Of   our   ev - er - last - ing   feast.
Thus may   all   our Sab-baths   be   Till we   rise to   reign with   Thee.

THE HAPPY LAND

The early Adventists—even after the disappointment of October 22, 1844—believed fully in the reality of heaven. For them it was more than just a promise of some far-off future bliss. The idea of heaven was of immediate relevance. In fact, it was an experience so real, so intoxicating that they could almost see and feel it already.

In 1858 Ellen White wrote in *Spiritual Gifts*, volume 1, a short chapter entitled "The Saints' Reward."

"Then I saw a very great number of angels bring from the city glorious crowns; a crown for every saint with his name written thereon; and as Jesus called for the crowns, angels presented them to Him, and the lovely Jesus, with His own right hand, placed the crowns on the heads of the saints. In the same manner, the angels brought the harps, and Jesus presented them also to the saints. The commanding angels first struck the note, and then every voice was raised in grateful, happy praise, and every hand skillfully swept over the strings of the harp, sending forth melodious music in rich and perfect strains.

"Then I saw Jesus lead the redeemed company to the gate of the city. He laid hold of the gate and swung it back on its glittering hinges, and bade the nations who had kept the truth to enter in. There was everything in the city to feast the eye. Rich glory they beheld everywhere. Then Jesus looked upon His redeemed saints; their countenances were radiant with glory; and as He fixed His loving eyes upon them, He said, with His rich musical voice, I behold the travail of my soul, and am satisfied. This rich glory is yours to enjoy eternally. Your sorrows are ended. There shall be no more death, neither sorrow, nor crying, neither shall there be any more pain. I saw the redeemed host bow and cast their glittering crowns at the feet of Jesus, and then, as His lovely hand raised them up, they touched their golden harps, and filled all heaven with their rich music, and songs to the Lamb.

"I then saw Jesus leading the redeemed host to the tree of life, and again we heard His lovely voice, richer than any music that ever fell on mortal ear, saying, The leaves of this tree are for the healing of the nations. Eat ye all of it. Upon the tree of life was the most beautiful fruit, which the saints could partake of freely. There was a most glorious throne in the city, and from under the throne proceeded a pure river of water of life, as clear as crystal. On either side of this river of life was the tree of life. On the banks of the river were beautiful trees bearing fruit which was good for food. Language is altogether too feeble to attempt a description of heaven. As the scene rises before me I am lost in amazement; and carried away with the surpassing splendor and the excellent glory, I lay down the pen, and exclaim, O what love! What wondrous love! The most exalted language cannot describe the glory of heaven nor the matchless depths of a Saviour's love" (pp. 209-211).

"Happy Land" was first published by Sabbathkeepers in the 1855 hymnal entitled *Hymns for Those Who Keep the Commandments of God and the Faith of Jesus*. No tune is suggested. The one being used here is from the 1886 *Hymns and Tunes*, the first hymnal to include a tune with the words. The same tune was retained in the 1941 *Church Hymnal*. Neither the author of the words nor the writer of the tune is listed in either *Hymns and Tunes* or the *Church Hymnal*. The tune is similar to that used by Joshua V. Himes when he published the hymn in his 1849 *Advent Harp*. It was not included in either the 1842 or 1843 edition of the *Millennial Harp*, so most likely was not used by the Millerite Adventists during their movement.

Actually, the tune came first in this hymn, and it stimulated the writing of the words. Andrew Young (1807-1889) was spending his vacation in 1838 on the Isle of Bute. While there he heard an Indian air called HAPPY LAND, which he liked very much. Being a Sunday school teacher, Young thought his students would enjoy it if only suitable words were available. Building on the tune HAPPY LAND, Young wrote the words to the hymn.

As anticipated, it proved very popular with the children who sang it. The text of the hymn is based on the words of Moses, "We are journeying unto the place of which the Lord said, I will give it you: come thou with us" (Num. 10:29).

The present melody WORLD TO COME was harmonized by a minister, James Gall (1808-1895). It appeared in *The Sacred Song Book* published in 1843.

The Happy Land

From Hymns for Those Who Keep
the Commanments of God ..., 1855

WORLD TO COME

1. There is a hap-py land, Far, far a-way,
2. Come to that hap-py land, Come, come a-way,
3. Bright in that hap-py land, Beams ev-ery eye;

Where saints in glo-ry stand, Bright, bright as day.
Why will ye doubt-ing stand, Why still de-lay.
Kept by a Fa-ther's hand, Love can-not die;

O how they sweet-ly sing, "Wor-thy is our Sav-ior King;"
O we shall hap-py be, From all sin and sor-row free;
Then shall Thy king-dom come, Saints shall have a glo-rious home;

Loud let His prais-es ring, Praise, praise for aye.
Lord, we shall live with Thee, Blest, blest for aye.
And, bright-er than the sun, Reign, reign for aye.

THE LORD IS COMING

It appears from 1 Corinthians 16:22 that the early Christians greeted each other with *"Maranatha,"* meaning "the Lord is coming." In the earliest days of our own church, the pioneers would also greet each other warmly on the rare occasions when they were able to meet and worship together.

In those early years, when the number of Sabbathkeepers was very small, they even practiced the holy kiss. In 1 Thessalonians 5:26, the apostle Paul says, "Greet all the brethren with an holy kiss." To our pioneers, Ellen White advised that "it should be regarded as a sign of fellowship to Christian friends when parting, and when meeting again after a separation of weeks or months." However, she went on to point out some other advice from the apostle Paul, "In the same chapter he says: 'Abstain from all appearance of evil.' There can be no appearance of evil when the holy kiss is given at a proper time and place." She reminded them, *"It is a holy kiss"* (*Early Writings*, p. 117).

Apparently some abused the salutation. In 1854 Ellen White wrote to one brother, "Dear Brother P[earsall], you have been indiscreet in practicing the salutation and have made little difference as to the time and place, whether you were surrounded by unbelievers or not, and have been ready to practice it too frequently, and no good but evil has resulted from it" (*Ellen G. White Manuscript Releases*, vol. 7, p. 208).

What had begun as a beautiful salutation between fellow believers was slowly abandoned because of abuse by a few of its practitioners and the misunderstanding that it caused among nonbelievers. Today, this old salutation hymn still speaks of the common belief in Christ's return that welds the hearts of Adventists together wherever they may be throughout the world.

This anonymously written hymn first appeared in a Sabbathkeeping Adventist hymnbook in 1852. James White included it in his second hymnal, *Hymns for Second Advent Believers*, which he published that year. The oldest known tune found for the hymn is WARRINGTON, composed in 1784 by Ralph Harrison (1748-1810) and last used with this hymn in the 1941 *Church Hymnal.*

The 1985 *Seventh-day Adventist Hymnal* committee chose to use a different, more familiar tune for these old words in the hope that the hymn might be sung more often. The well-known tune, THE SOLID ROCK, written by William B. Bradbury (1816-1868), was the tune selected. The new setting is the one used in *Early Advent Singing*.

The Lord Is Coming

I Cor. 16:22
Anon. c. 1849
St. 4 by Mary A. Steward, c. 1886

THE SOLID ROCK

William B. Bradbury, 1863 (1816-1868)

1. The Lord is com - ing, let this be The her - ald note of jub - i - lee; And when we meet and when we part The sal - u - ta - tion from the heart.
2. The Lord is com - ing! sound it forth From east to west, from south to north; Speed on! speed on the ti - dings glad, That none who love Him may be sad.
3. The Lord is com - ing, swift and sure And all His judg - ments shall en - dure, And none can hope to es - cape His wrath, Who walk not in the nar - row path.
4. This earth, with her ten thou-sand wrongs Will soon be tuned to no - bler songs; Our praise shall then, in realms of light, With all His u - ni - verse u - nite.

The Lord is com - ing, let this be The her - ald note of ju - bi - lee, The her - ald note of ju - bi - lee.

WASHING FEET

An anonymously written hymn that James White included in his 1849 hymnal, *Hymns for God's Peculiar People That Keep the Commandments of God and the Faith of Jesus*, is "Washing Feet." Since the Millerites did not practice foot washing, this was not a hymn they sang. The only comment included with the hymn in James White's first hymnal is the description "An Old Hymn." No tune is suggested to which it should be sung, so without music, it is impossible to know what tune the pioneers used when they sang it. In *Early Advent Singing* the words have been set to the tune "DUKE STREET" (*Seventh-day Adventist Hymnal*, No. 82, "Before Jehovah's Awful Throne").

The current *Seventh-day Adventist Hymnal* includes several tunes that were also used in the 1840s, all of which fit the words. Among those still in our current hymnal that doubtless would have been known to the pioneers are the tunes: HAMBURG (SDAH, No. 154, "When I Survey the Wondrous Cross"); HURSLEY (SDAH, No. 502, "Sun of My Soul"); and OLD HUNDREDTH (SDAH, No. 694, "Praise God, From Whom All Blessings").

All these tunes must be repeated once to fit the words of "Washing Feet" as printed by James White in the 1849 hymnal. When trying alternate tunes, it should be kept in mind that such might well have happened originally. Since organs and pianos were not then used by Sabbathkeepers, it is quite possible that song leaders in different places may have used various tunes for these same words, depending on what they knew and liked in their locale.

Although "Washing Feet" was never reprinted exactly as it appeared in the 1849 hymnal, it did continue to be reprinted in modified format in the 1852 through the 1861 hymnals, but always without music. It was last printed in Hymns and Tunes, first published in 1886. For the first time the words are printed with music. ZEPHYR was the tune used. Whether or not that tune was the one used earlier is unknown. If so, it too would have had to be repeated twice to accommodate the way James White printed the stanza in the 1849 hymnal. Since ZEPHYR was composed only in 1844, it seems doubtful that James White was already using it by 1849.*

Almost immediately after the disappointment of October 22,

1844, some of those who eventually started the Seventh-day Adventist Church began following Christ's example of foot washing at the time of commemorating the Lord's Supper. Originally they coupled with it the practice of the holy kiss (see under "The Lord Is Coming"). So foot washing came in very early in our history, and the ceremony has been observed immediately preceding the ordinance of the Lord's Supper ever since.

In 1854 Ellen White wrote the following counsel to those who were initiating the practice of foot washing in their own area:

"The washing of feet and partaking of the Lord's Supper should be more frequently practiced. Jesus set us an example, and told us to do as He had done. I saw that His example should be as exactly followed as possible; yet brethren and sisters have not always moved as judiciously as they should in washing feet, and confusion has been caused. It should be introduced into new places with carefulness and wisdom, especially where the people are not informed relative to the example and teachings of our Lord on this point, and where they have prejudice against it" (*Early Writings*, pp. 116, 117).

As she thought back on the practice of foot washing during the early days of the movement, Ellen White wrote in 1904:

"In the early days of the Advent movement, when our numbers were few, the celebration of the ordinances was made a most profitable occasion. On the Friday before, every church member endeavored to clear away everything that would tend to separate him from his brethren and from God. Hearts were closely searched; prayers for a divine revelation of hidden sin were earnestly offered; confessions of overreaching in trade, of ill-advised words hastily spoken, of sins cherished, were made. The Lord came near, and we were greatly strengthened and encouraged" (*Evangelism*, p. 274).

For Ellen White, "The ordinance of feet washing is an ordinance of service. This is the lesson the Lord would have all learn and practice. When this ordinance is rightly celebrated, the children of God are brought into holy relationship with each other, to help and bless each other" (*The SDA Bible Commentary*, Ellen G. White Comments, vol. 5, p. 1138).

---

* *The Seventh-day Adventist Hymn and Tune Book for Use in Divine Worship*, 1886, No. 1096. Two hymns are also set to the tune ZEPHYR in the 1941 *Church Hymnal*: Nos. 41 and 253, "O Christ, With Each Returning Morn" and "The Tempter to My Soul."

Washing Feet

From James White's
Hymns for God's Peculiar People ..., *1849*

DUKE STREET
John Hatton, (c. 1710-1793)

1. When Je - sus Christ was here be - low, He taught His
2. The Lord who made the earth and sky, A - rose and
3. Said Pet - er, Lord, it shall not be; Thou shalt not
4. Ye shall be hap - py, if ye know And do these

peo - ple what to do: And if we would His
laid His gar - ments by; And washed their feet to
stoop to wash - ing me: Oh! that no Chris - tian
things, by faith be - low; For I'll pro - tect you

pre - cepts keep, We must at - tend to wash - ing feet.
show that we, Like Christ, should al - ways hum - ble be.
now may say, I can - not Je - sus' word o - bey.
till I come, And then I'll take you to your home.

For on that night He was be - tray'd, He for us
He wash'd them all, though all were clean, Save Ju - das
Ye call me Lord and Mas - ter too; Then do as
The Lord of glo - ry stoops to men, And an ex -

139

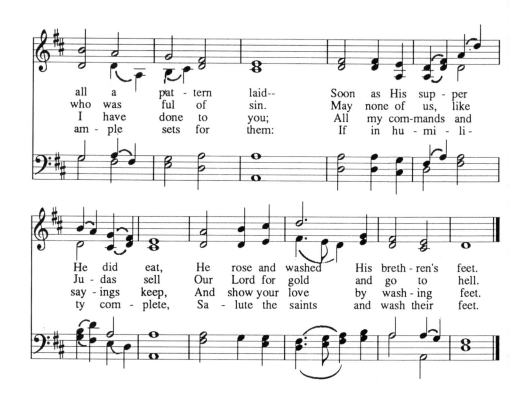

all   a   pat - tern   laid--   Soon   as His sup - per
who was   ful of   sin.   May none of us, like
I   have   done to   you;   All   my com-mands and
am - ple   sets for   them: If   in hu - mi - li -

He   did   eat,   He   rose and washed   His breth - ren's feet.
Ju - das   sell   Our Lord for gold   and go to   hell.
say - ings keep,   And show your love   by wash - ing   feet.
ty com - plete, Sa - lute the saints   and wash their   feet.

WE HAVE HEARD

This hymn sometimes has been described by Adventist historians as the first written by a Seventh-day Adventist, as well as the first to be published by one of our members. This is only partially correct.

"We Have Heard" was written by William H. Hyde, who for a brief time in 1845 was associated with James White, Ellen Harmon (later White), and the small group of former Millerites who became the nucleus of what became the Seventh-day Adventist Church. There is no evidence that Hyde was ever a Sabbathkeeper. In fact, James and Ellen White did not start keeping the Sabbath until shortly after their marriage in August 1846.

In 1845 William Hyde was present at a meeting at which Ellen received a vision that portrayed the new earth. He was so excited by her description of "The Better Land"—the name under which the hymn was first published—that he wrote this piece. Ellen White's vision is published in *Early Writings*, pages 17-20.

James White first published the hymn in his 1849 hymnbook *Hymns for God's Peculiar People That Keep the Commandments of God and the Faith of Jesus*. Although dated 1849, this small hymnal was not actually available for sale until early 1850. White reprinted the hymn in the November 1850 issue of *The Present Truth*. In 1851, when Ellen White's first booklet, *A Sketch of the Christian Experience and Views of Ellen G. White*, was printed, the four stanzas of this poem were printed on the outside of the back paper cover.

Knowing that his readers would be interested in the background of the hymn, James White put the following paragraph on the last page of the November 1850 issue of *The Present Truth*:

"Some may be interested in learning the origin of the hymn on the first page of this number. In the spring of 1845, the author of the vision, published in this paper, was very sick, nigh unto death. The elders of the church were finally called, and the directions of the apostle [James 5:14, 15] were strictly followed. God heard, answered, and healed the sick. The Holy Spirit filled the room, and she had a vision of the 'city,' 'life's pure river,' 'green fields,' 'roses of Sharon,' 'songs' of 'lovely birds,' the 'harps,' 'palms,' 'robes,' 'crowns,' the 'mount' Zion, the 'tree of life,' and the 'King of that country' mentioned in the hymn. A brother took up his pen, and in a very short time composed the hymn from the vision. It has been published in two or three Second Advent papers, Smith's collection of hymns, and finally found its way into the *Advent Harp*, published by J. V. Himes in 1849. Let those who 'despise prophesyings,' and reject the fulfillment of God's word in visions of the 'LAST DAYS,' remember, when they sing this hymn, that it was composed from a vision."

Even though William Hyde's hymn was written first, since he did not keep the Sabbath it would appear that the distinction of the first hymn to be written by a Sabbathkeeping Adventist actually goes to Heman S. Gurney, whose hymn, "Lo! An Angel Loud Proclaiming," was published by Joseph Bates in 1848. (See separate story under that hymn.) It was also Gurney's hymn that was actually the first to be printed in a Sabbathkeeping publication, since Bates's book came out approximately two years before White's hymnal.

In the spring of 1845 William Hyde became very sick with dysentery. A physician was called, and after examining him, felt Hyde's case was hopeless. Ellen and others visited Hyde and prayed for him. Hyde had previously become associated with some fanatics. He now broke his connection with them and in answer to repeated prayer was healed from his illness. As mentioned, William Hyde was present a short time later when Ellen was given the vision of the new earth that moved him to write this hymn.

Throughout her life Ellen White liked this hymn, doubtless because it reminded her of her early experience. During her later years, the members of her family would often hear her singing it as she went about her work. With a ring of triumph in her voice, she would sing the ending of the last stanza:

> We'll be there, we'll be there in a little while,
> We'll join the pure and the blest;
> We'll have the palm, the robe, the crown,
> And forever be at rest.

Unfortunately, it seems that by August 1845 William Hyde had returned to his former views, so he did not remain with the group that eventually became the Seventh-day Adventist Church. But his hymn has remained, though it is now seldom sung. It is the earliest-known hymn to be based on an Ellen White vision and has been printed in every one of our major hymnals since James White included it in his 1849 hymnal.

We Have Heard

W. H. Hyde, 1845

WE HAVE HEARD

1. We have heard from the bright, the ho - ly land, We have heard, and our hearts are glad; For we were a lone - ly pil - grim band, And wea -ry, and worn, and sad. They tell us the saints have a dwell - ing there-- No long - er are home - less ones; And we

2. They say green fields are wav - ing there, That nev - er a blight shall know; And the des - erts wild are bloom -ing fair, And the ros - es of Shar - on grow. There are love - ly birds in the bow - ers green, Their songs are blithe and sweet; And their

3. We have heard of the palms, the robes, the crowns, And the sil - ver - y band in white; Of the cit - y fair with pearl - y gates, All ra - di - ant with light. We have heard of the an - gels ra - di - ant with light. Their harps of gold how they sing; Of the

4. The King of that coun - try, He is fair, He's the joy and light of the place; In His beau - ty we shall be -hold Him there, And bask in His smil - ing face. We'll be there, we'll be there in a lit - tle while, We'll join the pure and the blest; We'll

143

know that the good - ly land is fair, Where life's pure riv - er runs.
warb - blings, gush-ing ev - er new, The an - gels harp - ings greet.
mount with the fruit - ful tree of life, Of the leaves that heal - ing bring.
have the palm, the robe, the crown, And for -ev - er be at rest.

WHAT HEAVENLY MUSIC

On one occasion in the 1880s, Ellen White was leading out in a prayer meeting at the St. Helena Sanitarium in northern California. As she often did when speaking, she had chosen a hymn appropriate to the topic of her presentation that evening. For some reason, when the congregation stood to sing, their hearts were not in the words they were mouthing. They sang listlessly, without any feeling, just as many congregations often still do.

Mrs White held up her hand to stop them. She said, "I have heard the angels sing. They do not sing as you are singing tonight. They sing with reverence. Their heart is in their expressions of song. They sing with meaning. Now let's try again and see if we can't put our hearts into the singing of this song" (Ellen G. White Document File 245-g; see also A. L. White, *Ellen G. White: The Lonely Years*, p. 384).

It is reported that when the congregation started to sing again, they put real feeling into the hymn she had chosen.

Through the 70 years of Ellen White's ministry she heard the angels sing a number of times in vision. (For some examples of those occasions, see under "In the Glad Time of the Harvest.") Not only did Mrs. White hear the angel choir, but she also gives us a verbal description of angelic singing. She says:

"I have been shown the order, the perfect order, of heaven, and have been enraptured as I listened to the perfect music there. . . . I have seen companies of angels, who stood in a hollow square, everyone having a harp of gold. . . . There is one angel who always leads, who first touches the harp and strikes the note, then all join in the rich, perfect music of heaven. It cannot be described. It is melody, heavenly, divine, while from every countenance beams the image of Jesus, shining with glory unspeakable" (*Testimonies*, vol. 1, p. 146).

Before his fall, Lucifer led the heavenly choir. And the singing of that choir, we are told, almost caused him to repent:

"The influence of the holy angels seemed for a time almost to carry him with them. As songs of praise ascended in melodious strains, swelled by thousands of glad voices, the spirit of evil seemed vanquished; unutterable love thrilled his entire being; his soul went out, in harmony with the sinless worshipers, in love to the Father and the Son. But again he was filled with pride in his own glory" (*Patriarchs and Prophets*, p. 37).

A number of times Ellen White heard such singing in vision. No wonder she wrote: "Music forms a part of God's worship in the courts above, and we should endeavor, in our songs of praise, to approach as nearly as possible to the harmony of the heavenly courts. . . . Singing, as a part of religious service, is as much an act of worship as is prayer" (*ibid.*, p. 594).

Many times Ella Robinson heard her grandmother say, "Children, we must learn to sing the songs of Zion here if we would join the angel choir yonder."

Looking to the future when the redeemed enter the New Jerusalem, Ellen White was shown:

"The gates of the City of God swing back upon their hinges, and the nations that have kept the truth enter in. There are the columns of angels on either side, and the ransomed of God walk in through the cherubim and seraphim. Christ bids them welcome and puts upon them His benediction. 'Well done, thou good and faithful servant: . . . enter thou into the joy of thy Lord. . . .'

"The crowns of immortal glory [are] upon their heads, and then the redeemed cast their glittering crowns at the feet of Jesus; and then the angelic choir strikes the note of victory, and the angels in the two columns take up the song, and the redeemed host join in as though they had been singing the song on the earth, and they have been.

"Oh, what music! There is not an inharmonious note. Every voice proclaims, 'Worthy is the Lamb that was slain' " (*The Seventh-day Adventist Bible Commentary*, Ellen G. White Comments, vol. 6, p. 1093).

"What Heavenly Music," when sung softly and reverently, reminds the singer of the heavenly choir that Ellen White saw and heard in vision. The hymn is one that James White included in his first 1849 hymnal. It had already been included in Joshua V. Himes's 60-page *Addition to the Supplement to the Millennial Harp*, printed in 1848 for Sundaykeeping Adventists. The tune was arranged by N. Billings. Prior to its inclusion in the 1985 *Seventh-day Adventist Hymnal*, this hymn last appeared in *Hymns and Tunes*, originally published in 1886. Commenting on the words of this hymn, Wayne Hooper writes, "This [hymn] is one of many that use the crossing of the Jordan as a metaphor for crossing over into the heavenly land, based on the text 'When ye are come to the brink of the water of Jordan' (Joshua 3:8). In some of these songs the inference is that death furnishes the instant of the crossover, but that is not according to the plain words of Scripture. On the other hand, the metaphor can apply to the Second Coming, when the redeemed cross the barrier between their long pilgrimage on earth and the heavenly Land of Promise. There they all join in 'heavenly music' with the angel choirs" (*Companion to the Seventh-day Adventist Hymnal*, p. 450).

What Heavenly Music

From James White's
Hymns for God's Peculiar People ..., 1849

HEAVENLY MUSIC
From Hymns and Tunes, 1886

1. What heav - en - ly mu - sic steals o - ver the sea!
2. On the banks of old Jor - dan here gaz - ing I stand,
3. Though dark are the wa - ters and rough is the wave,

En - tranc - ing the sens - es like sweet mel - o - dy!
And ear - nest - ly long - ing, I stretch forth my hand,
If Je - sus per - mit, the wild surg - es I'll brave;

'Tis the voice of the an - gels borne soft on the air;
Send a con - voy of an - gels, dear Je - sus, I pray!
For that heav - ven - ly mu - sic hath rav - ished me so,

For me they are sing - ing; their wel - come I hear.
Let me join that sweet mu - sic; come, take me a - way.
I must join in that cho - rus! I'll go! let me go!

148

WHEN I CAN READ
MY TITLE CLEAR

W. A. Spicer (1865-1952), secretary of the General Conference from 1903-1922, and then president from 1922-1930, remembered as a boy hearing James White (1821-1881) sing this hymn. Spicer tells about it in his book *Pioneer Days of the Advent Movement*, published in 1941:

"I remember well, as a boy, sitting in our church waiting for the preacher. Our backs were to the street door through which the minister would enter. Then suddenly the silence would be broken by a sweetly musical and strong, sure voice, singing a familiar hymn. I can see the singer now, James White, silver-haired, coming down the aisle, beating time on his Bible, and singing—

> 'When I can read my title clear
> To mansions in the skies,
> I'll bid farewell to ev'ry fear,
> And wipe my weeping eyes!'

"By the time he had finished the first stanza and the chorus, the congregation had been caught and carried along in the spirit of it, and was joining in—

> 'Let cares like a wild deluge come,
> And storms of sorrow fall;
> May I but safely reach my home,
> My God, my heaven, my all.'

"Some of the voices, in the seats where the elderly veterans sat, might have been a bit overworn, but I would like to hear such singing again" (pp. 146, 147).

For another story that mentions James White's use of the hymn "When I Can Read My Title Clear," see under "Is My Name Written There?" Also, for an additional account about James White starting a meeting while walking down the aisle and keeping time by clapping his Bible, see under "You Will See Your Lord a-Coming."

Besides being a compiler of several of our first Sabbathkeeping

Adventist hymnals, James White was also a good singer. In fact, his father, Deacon John White, had been a voice teacher. In White's autobiography, *Life Incidents*, published in 1868, he tells about an incident that happened when he was in his early 20s.

"In the autumn of that year [1843], in company with my father and two sisters, I attended the Maine Eastern Christian Conference, of which I was a member, held in the town of Knox. Before we reached the place, as night drew on, a heavy shower of rain compelled us to call at a hotel. In those days singing was our delight. My father had been a teacher of vocal music, and my sisters were first-class singers. And as time began to hang heavily upon our hands, we found relief in singing some of the most stirring revival melodies of those times.

"The landlord, his family, and many who had been driven in by the rain as we had been seemed to enjoy our singing, and when we had finished one piece, they would call for another. In this way the evening passed off pleasantly. And when my father called for our bill the next morning, the landlord told him there was none for him to settle, as we had paid him the evening before in singing. He also stated that at any time we would put up with him he would entertain us, and take his pay in singing" (pp. 104, 105).

In the 1886 *Hymns and Tunes*, this hymn by Isaac Watts was called "We'll Stand the Storm." The tune was arranged from the FREEDMEN by T. C. O'Kane. This same tune was used when the hymn was later reprinted in *Christ in Song*. The tune has been retained in *Early Advent Singing*.

The hymn first appeared in the 1852 hymnal published by James White. Although it was not published in the Millerite Adventist hymnals, Joshua V. Himes did include it in his 1849 *Advent Harp*, published for Sundaykeeping Adventists. The 1985 *Seventh-day Adventist Hymnal* has set the words to the tune PISGAH, a traditional American melody.

When I Can Read My Title Clear

2 Pet. 1:10

Isaac Watts (1674-1748)

Arr. from The Freedman

Tullius Clinton O'Kane (1830-1912)

bid fare-well to ev-ery fear, And wipe my weep - ing eyes.
I can smile at Sa-tan's rage, And face a frown -ing world.
I but safe - ly reach my home, My God, my heav'n, my all.
not a wave of trou-ble roll, A - cross my peace - ful breast.

Refrain

We will stand the storm, We will an - chor
We will stand, stand the storm, It will not be ver-y long, We will an-chor by and

by and by, by and by; We will stand the
by, We will an -chor by and by; We will stand, stand the storm, It will

storm,
not be ver - y long, We will an - chor by and by by and by).

EARLY SEVENTH-DAY ADVENTIST HYMNS

1863-1915

EARLY SEVENTH-DAY ADVENTIST HYMNS

The first official Seventh-day Adventist hymnal was printed six years after the founding of the General Conference in 1863. The 1869 *Hymns and Tunes for Those That Keep the Commandments of God and the Faith of Jesus* contained 424 pages.

Several hymn writers contributed to Adventist hymnody during these years. Among them was Roswell F. Cottrell (1814-1892), a former Seventh Day Baptist who had become a Sabbathkeeper about 1851. The most prolific writer was Ellen White's nephew, Franklin E. Belden (1858-1945), the son of her older sister, Sarah.

Then there were James and Ellen White's two oldest boys, Henry and James Edson, who were both musical. Unfortunately, Henry died late in 1863 at the age of 16, but when Edson grew older he wrote music and published several hymns. In fact, his *Song Anchor, a Choice Collection of Favorites for Sabbath School and Praise Service*, published in 1878, was the first Seventh-day Adventist hymnal to include music for each hymn.

Edwin S. Barnes, music teacher at Battle Creek College for several years, contributed a number of hymn tunes, though he apparently did not write the words for any hymns.

For a complete discussion of the music, including a listing of all the hymnals, from this era of the denomination's history, see the historical introduction in *Companion to the Seventh-day Adventist Hymnal*, by Wayne Hooper and Edward E. White.

A partial list of the more prominent hymnals issued between the founding of the General Conference in 1863 and the death of Ellen White in 1915 would include the following:

1869   *Hymns and Tunes for Those Who Keep the Commandments of God and the Faith of Jesus*, Steam Press of the Seventh-day Adventist Publishing Association, Battle Creek, Michigan, 424 pages.

1872   *Hymns and Spiritual Songs for Camp-Meetings and other Religious Gatherings (Hymns and Spiritual Songs)*, Steam Press

155

of the Seventh-day Adventist Publishing Association, Battle Creek, Michigan, 192 pages.

1876   *Hymns and Tunes for Those Who Keep the Commandments of God and the Faith of Jesus* (*Spiritual Songs*), Steam Press of the Seventh-day Adventist Publishing Association, Battle Creek, Michigan, 416 pages.

1878   *Hymns of Praise for Use at Lectures and Revival Meetings*, Pacific Press Publishing House, Oakland, California, 64 pages.

1878   James Edson White, *Song Anchor, a Choice Collection of Favorites for Sabbath School and Praise Gatherings* (*Song Anchor*), Pacific Press Publishing Association, Oakland, California, 159 pages.

1880   James Edson White, *Temperance and Gospel Songs for the Use of Temperance Clubs and Gospel Temperance Meetings* (*Temperance and Gospel Songs*), American Health and Temperance Association, Battle Creek, Michigan, 100 pages.

1881   J. E. White; C. W. Stone; A. B. Oyen, *Better Than Pearls, Sacred Songs Expressly Adapted for Gospel Meetings* (*Better Than Pearls*), published by J. E. White, 133 West Main Street, Battle Creek, Michigan, 112 pages.

1882   D. S. Hakes, *Pearly Portals for the Sabbath School* (*Pearly Portals*), published by G. D. Russell, Boston; and Pacific Press Publishing Company, Oakland, California, 160 pages.

1886   *Seventh-day Adventist Hymn and Tune Book for Use in Divine Worship* (*1886 Hymns and Tunes*), Review and Herald Publishing House, Battle Creek, Michigan, 1413 hymns on 640 pages.

1886   James Edson White, *Joyful Greeting for the Sabbath School* (*Joyful Greetings*), The J. E. White Publishing Company, Battle Creek, Michigan, 216 pages.

1891   Franklin E. Belden, *Songs of Freedom*, National Religious
        Liberty Association, New York, 100 pages.

1892   Lillie Affolter, F. E. Belden, *Bible Object Lessons and Songs for
        Little Ones* (*Bible Object Lessons*), Bible Kindergarten and
        Gospel Music House, Chicago, 159 pages.

1894   *The Gospel Song Sheaf for Sabbath Schools and Young People's
        Meetings* (*Gospel Song Sheaf*), Pacific Press Publishing
        Company, Oakland, California, 240 pages.

1900   Franklin E. Belden, *Christ in Song*, Review and Herald
        Publishing Company, Battle Creek, Michigan, 413 pages.

1908   Franklin E. Belden, *Christ in Song* (revised and
        enlarged), Review and Herald Publishing Association,
        Washington, D.C., 576 pages.

Many of the gospel hymns and other pieces that are still sung in
the Adventist Church were introduced during these years. Rather
than attempting to list all of them, what follows is a list of hymns
from that era that were actually written by Seventh-day Adventists
and are still used, and are found in the 1985 *Seventh-day Adventist
Hymnal*. (The two hymns marked with asterisks are included in *Early
Advent Singing*.)

    Words only:
        Fannie Bolton (18?-1926)
            570   Not I, but Christ

        Roswell F. Cottrell (1814-1892)
            179   The Wonders of Redeeming Love
            417   O Solemn Thought

        Mrs. L. D. Avery-Stuttle (1855-1933)
            554   O Let Me Walk With Thee

    Music only:
        Edwin Barnes (1864-1930)
            6   O Worship the Lord

554   O Let Me Walk With Thee

Frank E. Belden (1858-1945)
359   Hark! the Voice of Jesus Calling
494   We Would See Jesus
528   A Shelter in the Time of Storm
653   Lead Them, My God, to Thee

James Edson White (1849-1928)
281   I Gave My Life for Thee

Words and music:
Frank E. Belden
183   I Will Sing of Jesus' Love
253   There's No Other Name Like Jesus
308   Wholly Thine
412   Cover With His Life*
416   The Judgment Has Set
430   Joy By and By
531   We'll Build on the Rock
579   'Tis Love That Makes Us Happy*
595   Let Every Lamp Be Burning
596   Look for the Waymarks
600   Hold Fast Till I Come
604   We Know Not the Hour

COVER WITH HIS LIFE

By far the most prolific Seventh-day Adventist hymn writer of the nineteenth century was Franklin E. Belden, the son of Ellen White's older sister, Sarah. Born in 1858, Frank was already writing hymns by the time he was in his early 20s. He wrote several hundred during his lifetime.

To give some idea of just how talented Belden was, it is reported that he could write a hymn in as short as an hour's time. His daughter recalled her father going to Colorado to help in evangelistic work. While there he would listen as the minister would read a text to start his sermon. Belden would then slip out and write a new hymn based on the text. By the time the sermon was finished, Belden and his wife, who was also a musician, would stand and sing a new hymn based on the sermon text.

In 1888 Frank Belden went to the General Conference session in Minneapolis. Unfortunately, he did not accept righteousness by faith there. Later his aunt Ellen White wrote several letters to him from Australia, where she lived from 1891 to 1900. One ran to 15 pages in length. In her letters, she appealed to Frank to improve his relationship with God. For a time it seemed that he was making progress, but later he seemed to slip back into his old ways, especially after he felt that he had been wronged in some business dealings with the church. Though his aunt Ellen agreed that some of his complaints were justified, she still urged him not to let it affect his Christian experience. This supposed grievance laid the foundation for a course of action that led to his separation from the church about 1907. The last years of his life he was antagonistic toward the church of his youth.

During his career in the denomination, Belden either compiled or assisted in compiling several hymnbooks. Among these were *Hymns and Tunes* (1886), *Joyful Greetings for the Sabbath School* (1886), *Songs of Freedom* (1891), and *Gospel Song Sheaf* (1894). Probably the most popular hymnbook ever used in the Seventh-day Adventist Church was his *Christ in Song*. It was first published in 1900 and was revised and enlarged in 1908. In most churches it supplanted *Hymns and Tunes*, the official hymnal of the church at the time. For more than 30 years a whole generation of Adventists used *Christ in Song* and loved its hymns.

"Cover With His Life" sounds a warning to each of us. It is apparent from the words that Frank Belden understood the theory of righteousness by faith as he wrote this hymn. Sadly, although he knew the principles, it appears that he may never have actually accepted Christ's righteousness in his own life. One may wonder how such could be possible, but Frank Belden's experience serves as a warning to all. It is entirely possible for religion to become merely a habit—we may know all the right answers to the questions, but that is as deep as it goes.

Both the words and tune for "Cover With His Life" were written in 1899. F. E. Belden included the hymn in both the 1900 edition of *Christ in Song* and the expanded and revised edition that he brought out in 1908.

Cover With His Life

F. E. Belden, 1899 (1858-1945)

F. E. Belden, 1899

1. Look up-on Je - sus, sin-less is He; Fa-ther, im - pute His
2. Deep are the wounds trans-gres-sion has made; Red are the stains; my
3. Long-ing the joy of par-don to know; Je-sus holds out a
4. Re -con-ciled by His death for my sin, Jus - ti - fied by His

life un - to me. My life of scar - let, my sin and woe,
soul is a - fraid. O to be cov - ered, Je-sus, with Thee,
robe white as snow; "Lord, I ac - cept it! leav-ing my own,
life pure and clean, Sanc-ti-fied by o - bey-ing His word,

Refrain

Cov-er with His life, whit -er than snow.
Safe from the law that now judg-eth me!
Glad-ly I wear Thy pure life a - lone." Cov - er with His life,
Glo-ri -fied when re - turn - eth my Lord.

whit-er than snow; Full -ness of His life then shall I know;

My life of scar - let, my sin and woe, Cov-er with His life, whiter than snow.

EAS-6

DARE TO BE A DANIEL

B oth the words and music of this temperance hymn were written in 1873 by Philipp Bliss (1838-1876). At the time, he was teaching a Sunday school class in the First Congregational church in Chicago. Bliss wrote the hymn, based on Daniel 1:8, especially for his class.

The first Seventh-day Adventist hymnal to include the hymn was *Temperance and Gospel Songs*, published in 1880. It continued to be included in major Adventist hymnals through the 1941 *Church Hymnal*.

On Sunday afternoon, July 24, 1881, Ellen White spoke on the subject of temperance in Charlotte, Michigan. It was a favorite theme of hers. Later, she recalled that after her remarks, her husband, James, "united with others in singing the stirring song 'Dare to Be a Daniel!' I was surprised," she said, "at the power and spirit with which he sang."

James, ill with a cold, returned with Ellen to Battle Creek the following Wednesday. Although complaining of a headache, he went on into the office as usual. Every morning the two of them went to the grove near their house to pray. During their season of prayer on Sabbath morning James "seemed reluctant to cease pleading with God for special guidance and blessing." They then went to the Tabernacle, where he opened the services with singing and prayer. It would be the last time that he ever stood in the pulpit beside his wife. On the following Sabbath, August 6, 1881, just after 5:00 p.m., James White died of "malarial fever" in the Battle Creek Sanitarium. He was just two days past his sixtieth birthday.

Ellen White must have liked this song because she continued referring to it in articles and sermons the rest of her life. Sometimes she merely used the expression "Dare to be a Daniel, dare to stand alone," though at other times she quoted the entire first stanza.

At an Australian camp meeting at Geelong, Victoria, Ellen White once again spoke on temperance, on Sunday afternoon, March 11, 1900. Later she recalled, "I spoke in the afternoon . . . , taking the first chapter of Daniel as my text. All listened attentively, seeming surprised to hear temperance presented from the Bible. After dwelling on the integrity and firmness of the Hebrew captives,

I asked the choir to sing—

> 'Dare to be a Daniel,
>   Dare to stand alone;
>   Dare to have a purpose firm;
>   Dare to make it known!'

"The inspiring notes of this song rang out from the singers on the stand, who were joined by the congregation. I then resumed my talk, and I know that before I had finished, many present had a better understanding of the meaning of Christian temperance" (*Review and Herald*, May 22, 1900).

Ten years later, in the January 25, 1910, issue of *The Youth's Instructor*, in one of Ellen White's last articles, she wrote especially for young people:

"Every youth needs to cultivate decision. . . . Be firm, else you will find your house—your character—built upon a sandy foundation. . . .

"Many there are who are changed by every current. They wait to hear what some one else thinks, and his opinion is often accepted as altogether true. They do not say, 'Lord, I cannot make any decision until I know Thy will.' If these youth would lean wholly upon God, they would grow strong in His strength.

"We are not to fashion ourselves by the world's criterion or after the world's type. 'Dare to be a Daniel; dare to stand alone.' . . .

"Have courage to do the right. Possess an individuality of your own. If you would succeed in anything that is elevating and ennobling, you must cultivate firmness for the right."

Dare to Be a Daniel

Daniel 1:8

P. P. Bliss, 1873 (1838-1876)

DANIEL

P. P. Bliss, 1873

1. Stand-ing by a pur - pose true, Heed - ing God's com - mand,
2. Man - y might - y men are lost, Dar - ing not to stand,
3. Man - y gi - ants great and tall, Stalk - ing thro' the land,
4. Hold the tem-perance ban - ner high! On to vic - tory grand!

Hon - or them, the faith - ful few, All hail to Dan-iel's band!
Who for God had been a host By join - ing Dan-iel's band!
Head-long to the earth would fall If met by Dan-iel's band!
Sa - tan and his host de - fy, And shout for Dan-iel's band!

Refrain

Dare to be a Dan - iel, Dare to stand a - lone!

Dare to have a pur-pose firm! Dare to make it known!

164

HOW SWEET ARE THE TIDINGS

This anonymously written old Adventist hymn has long been a favorite. It initially appeared in the 1869 hymnal. That might properly be considered the first official hymnal of the Seventh-day Adventist Church, since it was the first to be published under the authorization of the General Conference after its organization in 1863. All of our earlier hymnals had been compiled by James White, occasionally with the assistance of others, except for the one published for youth and children in 1854 by James's sister, Anna White.

No source for the words to this hymn has been discovered, but the tune was originally written to accompany a popular ballad of that era called "Bonny Eloise." It had been composed by John Roger Thomas in 1858. The song was taken up by both Northern and Southern military bands during the Civil War. The tune has been altered only slightly for use with "How Sweet Are the Tidings." This is another example of the practice at that time of putting religious words with secular tunes. (See discussion under "O Brother, Be Faithful.")

The original secular words, written by G. W. Elliott, are in praise of a young girl who lived in the Mohawk Valley of New York State near the Mohawk River.

Bonny Eloise

O, sweet is the vale where the Mohawk gently glides
    On its clear winding way to the sea,
And dearer than all storied streams on earth besides,
    Is this bright rolling river to me;

Chorus:
But sweeter, dearer, yes, dearer far than these
    Who charm where others all fail,
Is blue-eyed, bonny, bonny Eloise,
    The belle of the Mohawk Vale.

O, sweet are the scenes of my boyhood's sunny years,
    That bespangle the gay valley o'er,
And dear are the friends seen thro' memories' fond tears
    That have lived in the blest days of yore.

O, sweet are the moments when dreaming I roam,
    Thro' my loved haunts now mossy and grey,
And dearer than all is my childhood's hallowed home,
    That is crumbling now slowly away.

Though the Civil War era song "Bonny Eloise" has generally been long forgotten by society, the tune is preserved among Adventists when they sing this hymn that contrasts loneliness, sorrow, and death with the glorious hope of Christ's soon return.

How Sweet Are the Tidings

Anon

BONNIE ELOISE
Arr. from John R. Thomas, 1858

1. How sweet are the ti - dings that greet the pil-grim's ear, As he
2. The mos - sy old graves where the pil - grims sleep Shall be
3. There we'll meet, ne'er to part in our hap - py E - den home, Sweet
4. Hal - le - lu - jah, A - men! hal - le - lu - jah a - gain! Soon if

wan - ders in ex - ile from home! Soon, soon will the Sav - ior in
o - pen as wide as be - fore, And the mil - lions that sleep in the
songs of re - demp-tion we'll sing; From the north, from the south, all the
faith - ful we all shall be there; O, be watch - ful, be hope - ful, be

glo - ry ap - pear, And soon will the king - dom come.
might - y deep Shall live on this earth once more.
ran - somed shall come, And wor - ship our heaven - ly King.
joy - ful till then, And a crown of bright glo - ry we'll wear.

He's com - ing, com - ing, com - ing soon I know, Com - ing

back to the earth a - gain; And the wea - ry pil - grim

will to glo - ry go, When the Sav - ior comes to reign,

IN THE GLAD TIME
OF THE HARVEST

According to Ellen White's oldest granddaughter, Ella (White) Robinson, "Once, after listening quietly as we sang 'In the Glad Time of the Harvest,' [Grandmother] remarked that there was a strain in that song which reminded her of songs she had heard the angels sing when in heavenly vision."

Many times during the 70 years of Ellen White's ministry, she was privileged while in vision to hear the angels sing. In fact, in a vision given her in 1850, she was even allowed to sing with the angels. Ellen White wrote, "Then I was pointed to the glory of heaven, to the treasure laid up for the faithful. Everything was lovely and glorious. The angels would sing a lovely song, then they would cease singing and take their crowns from their heads and cast them glittering at the feet of the lovely Jesus, and with melodious voices cry, 'Glory, Alleluia!' I joined with them in their songs of praise and honor to the Lamb, and every time I opened my mouth to praise Him, I felt an unutterable sense of the glory that surrounded me. It was a far more, an exceeding and eternal weight of glory. Said the angel, 'The little remnant who love God and keep His commandments and are faithful to the end will enjoy this glory and ever be in the presence of Jesus and sing with the holy angels' " (*Early Writings*, p. 66).

Members of Ellen White's family recalled that occasionally when she came from her bedroom in the morning, she would ask, "Did you hear the angel choir singing last night?" And they would tell her they had not. It was their belief that God sometimes sent the angel choir to sing to her in vision, to lift at least momentarily the heavy burden that He knew she bore being His messenger.

Ellen White describes one such experience that occurred at her Elmshaven home in northern California in 1907. She records what happened in *Testimonies for the Church*, volume 9, pages 65 and 66:

"The afternoon of March 2 I spent in counsel with Brother and Sister S. N. Haskell, discussing the work in Oakland and their plans to go East to spend some time in South Lancaster [Massachusetts]. After our visit I was weary and retired early. I was suffering with rheumatism in my left side and could get no rest because of the pain. I turned from side to side, trying to find ease from the suffering. There was pain in my heart that portended no good for me. At last I fell asleep.

"About half past nine I attempted to turn myself, and as I did so, I became aware that my body was entirely free from pain. As I turned from side to side, and moved my hands, I experienced an extraordinary freedom and lightness that I cannot describe. The room was filled with light, a most beautiful, soft, azure light, and I seemed to be in the arms of heavenly beings.

"This peculiar light I have experienced in the past in times of special blessing, but this time it was more distinct, more impressive, and I felt such peace, peace so full and abundant no words can express it. I raised myself into a sitting posture, and I saw I was surrounded by a bright cloud, white as snow, the edges of which were tinged with a deep pink. The softest, sweetest music was filling the air, and I recognized the music as the singing of the angels. Then a Voice spoke to me, saying: 'Fear not; I am your Saviour. Holy angels are all about you.'

" 'Then this is heaven!' I said, 'and now I can be at rest. I shall have no more messages to bear, no more misrepresentations to endure. Everything will be easy now, and I shall enjoy peace and rest. Oh, what inexpressible peace fills my soul! Is this indeed heaven? Am I one of God's little children? and shall I always have this peace?'

"The Voice replied: 'Your work is not yet done.'

"Again I fell asleep, and when I awoke I heard music and I wanted to sing. Then someone passed my door, and I wondered if the person saw the light. [There is no evidence that they did see it.] After a time the light passed away, but the peace remained."

After falling asleep again, Ellen White was given a vision about the publishing work.

"In the Glad Time of the Harvest" first appeared in *Hymns and Tunes*, published in 1886. The title used in both that hymnal and the later *Christ in Song* was "When the King Shall Claim His Own." In the 1941 *Church Hymnal* the title was changed to "In the Glad Time of the Harvest," though the words remained unchanged.

Both author and composer of this hymn were Seventh-day Adventists. Lorenzo D. Santee (1845-1919) was born in Hornellsville, New York. Ordained a minister in 1876, he worked mainly in the Illinois Conference. Through the years he wrote a number of poems, including some that were published in the *Review and Herald*.

This "hymn breathes the fervor of the Adventists who preached their distinctive doctrines of the millennium, which was to begin at Christ's second coming at the close of the investigative judgment" (Edward. E. White, *Singing With Understanding*, p. 367). The Scripture basis for the hymn is, "For the Son of man shall come in the glory of his Father, with his angels; and then he shall reward every man according to his works" (Matt. 16:27). At least eight other texts are also referred to in the hymn.

The tune WHEN THE KING SHALL CLAIM HIS OWN was composed by Edwin E. Barnes (1864-1930) in 1886. Born in England, Barnes came to the United States at the age of 17 to become theorganist at the Dime Tabernacle in Battle Creek, Michigan. Continuing musical studies in voice, piano, and organ, he later headed the music department at Battle Creek College for nearly 20 years. Still later, Barnes served as organist and choir director for the First Congregational Church in Battle Creek for more than 30 years.

In the Glad Time of the Harvest

Matt. 16:27

Lorenzo D. Santee (1845-1919)
Edwin Barnes (1864-1930)

1. In the glad time of the har-vest, In the grand mil-len-ial year,
2. O the rap-ture of His peo-ple! Long they've dwelt on earth's low sod,
3. Long they've toiled with-in the har-vest, Sown the prec-ious seed with tears;
4. We shall greet the loved and lov-ing, Who have left us lone-ly here;

When the King shall take His scep-ter, And to judge the world ap-pear,
With their hearts e'er turn-ing homeward, Rich in faith and love to God.
Soon they'll drop their heav-y bur-dens In the glad mil-len-ial years;
Ev-ery heart-ache will be ban-ished When the Sav-ior shall ap-pear;

Earth and sea shall yield their trea-sure, All shall stand be-fore the throne;
They will share the life im-mor-tal, They will know as they are known,
They will share the bliss of hea-ven, Nev-er-more to sigh or moan;
Nev-er grieved with sin or sor-row, Nev-er wea-ry or a-lone;

Just a-wards will then be giv-en,
They will pass the pear-ly por-tal, When the King shall claim His own.
Star-ry crowns will then be giv-en,
O, we long for that glad mor-row

172

IS MY NAME WRITTEN THERE?

In the days prior to the use of public-address systems, rainstorms could cause a real problem for speakers. They found it difficult to be heard, especially while preaching in tents. Ellen White found herself in such a situation at the Newcastle, New South Wales, camp meeting in Australia in 1898.

There had been a serious question in the minds of the conference officials as to whether they should even try to hold a camp meeting that year. The previous year, a very successful one had been held at Stanmore, not too far from Sydney, but the expense of that meeting had left the conference in debt. So it seemed best in 1898 to forgo a camp meeting for lack of funds.

Finally, the proposal was made to hold a meeting in Newcastle. The site chosen was only about 25 miles from Cooranbong, where Avondale College had opened the previous year. As things turned out, the large conference tent that they planned on using was needed in Melbourne, so a new tent was rented for the Newcastle meetings. It cost them £15 Australian, with the option to purchase the tent if money could be raised to meet the price. Ellen White described it as a "very large tent, the largest we have ever had the privilege of speaking under." George B. Starr said in his report of the meetings that it was "the largest pavilion yet used by our people in these colonies."

For several months, Herbert Lacey had been holding evangelistic meetings in Newcastle. So, whereas the organizers of the camp meeting thought they might get 100 Adventist members to attend (from a conference membership of 400), plus a few from the city, on opening night, Thursday, December 22, there were 1,000 people present. Two hundred of them were Adventists.

Ellen White, accompanied by Sara McEnterfer, drove over to the camp meeting from Cooranbong on Friday. It was a hot and oppressive day. But weather conditions changed that night. A rainstorm came up that continued on through Sabbath. Ellen White described the situation at the campground:

"We have had a terrible tempest of rain and wind. It did bad work for our small tents, but the large tent was new, and staked with poles and cross poles inside, so that it would be difficult to blow down. . . . The wind became a howling gale, and continued over the

Sabbath. Sabbath the rain just poured down, as if the windows of heaven were opened. Nevertheless our meetings went on, and there was a good attendance from the camp. Men had to leave the meeting and attend to securing the tents in the tempest of wind and rain" (letter 129, 1898; quoted in A. L. White, *Ellen G. White: The Australian Years*, p. 372).

The speaker at the Sabbath afternoon meeting was Ellen White. In spite of the downpour outside, a large audience crowded into the tent. When the storm raged too fiercely so that the speaker could not be heard, the congregation sang. Ellen White recalled, "When the rain came down in torrents, we poured out our thanksgiving in songs of praise" (*Review and Herald*, Apr. 11, 1899). Apparently this happened several times that afternoon, as the meeting lasted from 3:00 to nearly sundown. Among the hymns they sang during those torrential downpours were "Is My Name Written There?" "The Evergreen Shore" (*Hymns and Tunes*, No. 1365; *Christ in Song*, No. 909), and "When the Mists Have Rolled Away" (*Hymns and Tunes*, No. 1354; *Christ in Song*, No. 893).

Ellen White used the storm as an example of what "the Lord will do for His people in letting the latter rain of His rich blessing in truth and righteousness fall upon them" (*Review and Herald*, Apr. 11, 1890). She also extended a call for those who wanted to consecrate themselves to the Lord to do so, and several responded. In spite of the rain, many testified that it was the best Sabbath they had ever enjoyed.

Years earlier, James White found himself in a similar situation while trying to speak one evening at a camp meeting. The rain began falling, making it all but impossible to be heard.

"Let's sing while we wait for the storm to subside," James suggested. "It won't last long." The song he suggested was most appropriate, "We'll Stand the Storm" (also called "When I Can Read My Title Clear," *Early Advent Singing*, No. 35). Sure enough, before long the rain stopped and White was able to resume his sermon. He became so completely absorbed in what he was saying that he walked right off the platform. But this did not deter him. He picked himself up and climbed back up onto the platform, all the while still preaching! In fact, he built the incident right into his sermon so well that many in the audience thought he had planned it that way.

The words to "Is My Name Written There?" were written by Mrs. Ann Kidder, nee Pepper (1820-1905), a Baptist from Boston who spent more than half her life living in New York City. During her long life she wrote about 1,000 hymns.

The tune was composed by Frank Marion Davis (1839-1897) in July 1876. He was a piano teacher, solo singer, choir leader, and publisher of Sunday school and temperance songs.

The hymn first appears in a Seventh-day Adventist hymnal, *Better Than Pearls*, compiled by James Edson White, C. W. Stone, and A. B. Oyen, and printed in 1881. That hymnal was expressly designed for use in gospel meetings. The last songbook to contain the hymn was the *Church Hymnal*, published in 1941.

Luke 10: 20 # Is My Name Written There?

Mrs. Mary Ann Kidder, née Pepper (1820-1905)   *Frank Marion Davis (1839-1897)*

1. Lord, I care not for rich - es, Neith-er sil - ver nor gold; I would make sure of heav - en, I would en - ter the fold; In the book of Thy king - dom, With its pag - es so fair, Tell me, Je - sus, my Sav - ior, Is my name writ - ten there?

2. Lord, my sins they are man - y, Like the sands of the sea, But Thy blood, O my Sav - ior, Is suf - fi - cient for me; For Thy prom - ise is writ - ten In bright let - ters that glow, "Tho' your sins be as scar - let, I will make them like snow."

3. Oh, that beau - ti - ful cit - y, With its man-sions of light, With its glo - ri - fied be - ings In pure gar - ments of white; Where no ev - il thing com - eth To de - spoil what is fair, Where the an - gels are watch-ing-- Is my name writ - ten there?

Is my name writ - ten there, On the page white and fair? In the book of Thy king-dom, Is my name writ - ten there?

JESUS, LOVER OF MY SOUL

This beautiful hymn was Ellen G. White's favorite. She spent much of her adult life writing and speaking about Christ and His work. Thousands and thousands of times she used His name in her writings. In 1877 and 1878 she brought out two volumes on His life, *Spirit of Prophecy*, volumes 2 and 3. These were the forerunners of her expanded biography of Christ published in 1898, *The Desire of Ages*. She also brought out *Thoughts From the Mount of Blessing* in 1896 and *Christ's Object Lessons* in 1900. In addition to these, over the years she wrote several pamphlets that focused specifically on Christ and His ministry.

The Desire of Ages took many years to complete. All the traveling she did, the talks she gave, and the letters she wrote continually delayed Ellen White in writing her book. Her diary entry for July 15, 1892, written in Preston, Melbourne, Australia, gives a glimpse into her own feelings as she worked on her masterpiece about Christ:

"The Lord has brought me through another night. I did not sleep well. The weather this winter has not been unpleasant; but the air is very penetrating, and I cannot manage to keep comfortably warm in these high rooms, with only a grate fire. I have had two severe chills, and this has greatly increased the lameness in my shoulders and hips. But notwithstanding this, I was able to spend most of yesterday writing on the life of Christ. I praise the Lord because I feel a nearness to my Saviour. My faith feeds on the rich promises of God, which are full of comfort and hope. [Here she quotes "Jesus, Lover of My Soul."]

"My whole being longs after the Lord. I am not content to be satisfied with occasional flashes of light. I must have more. 'If any man thirst,' Christ said, 'let him come unto me, and drink' (John 7:37). 'The water that I shall give him shall be in him a well of water springing up into everlasting life' (John 4:14)" (*Ellen G. White Manuscript Releases*, vol. 19, pp. 292, 293).

When Ellen White prayed, she spoke to God as to a friend. Various ones who heard her pray recalled that she did not begin her prayer with "Our Father," but rather "My Father." Both the Father and His Son were like close personal friends to her.

Of all her recollections of her grandmother, Ella Robinson said that her favorite happened on a Sabbath when Mrs. White was preaching. That particular morning Ellen was talking about the matchless love of Jesus for each one of us. As she was talking, she paused in the middle of her presentation. It was almost as if for a moment she forgot that she was standing in front of a congregation of people. She stood there and looked up as if she were looking right into the face of Jesus and said, "Oh, Jesus, how I love You. How I love You. How I love You." Ella recalled that a deep hush came over the audience—heaven seemed very near.

"Jesus, Lover of My Soul" was written in 1740 by Charles Wesley (1707-1788). The original third stanza is now omitted:

> 3. Wilt Thou not regard my call?
>   Wilt Thou not accept my prayer?
> Lo, I sink, I faint, I fall,
>   Lo, on Thee I cast my care.
> Reach me out Thy gracious hand,
>   While I of Thy strength receive,
> Hoping against hope I stand,
>   Dying, and behold, I live.

The tune apparently favored by Ellen White was composed by Simeon Butler Marsh (1798-1875) of Sherburne, New York. It is called MARTYN.

The Millerites did not include this hymn in their hymnals. The first Seventh-day Adventist hymnal that contained it was the one published in 1869. Only two stanzas were printed, and no music was included. In 1872 James White printed all four stanzas in the last hymnal he compiled, called *Hymns and Spiritual Songs*, but to a different tune than the one used here.

James Edson White also included the hymn in the second edition of his *Song Anchor*, published in 1878. However, he used a tune that D. S. Hakes had written that year. It was not until *Hymns and Tunes* was published in 1886 that a Seventh-day Adventist hymnal connected the tune MARTYN with these words.

Jesus, Lover of My Soul

MARTYN

Charles Wesley, 1740 (1707-1788)

Simeon B. Marsh, 1834, alt. (1798-1835)

1. Je - sus, lov - er of my soul, Let me to Thy bos - om fly,
2. Oth - er ref - uge have I none, Hangs my help-less soul on Thee;
3. Thou, O Christ, art all I want, More than all in Thee I find;
4. Plenteous grace with Thee is found-- Grace to par-don all my sin;

While the bil -lows near me roll, While the tem-pest still is high;
Leave, O leave me not a - lone! Still support and com - fort me;
Raise the fal - len, cheer the faint, Heal the sick, and lead the blind.
Let the heal - ing streams a - bound, Make and keep me pure with - in;

Hide me, O my Sav - ior, hide! Till the storm of life is past;
All my trust on Thee is stayed, All my help from Thee I bring;
Just and ho - ly is Thy name, I am all un - righ -teous-ness;
Thou of life the Foun - tain art, Free - ly let me take of Thee;

Safe in - to the ha - ven guide, O re-ceive my soul at last!
Cov - er my de - fense -less head With the shad -ow of Thy wing.
Vile and full of sin I am, Thou art full of truth and grace.
Spring Thou up with - in my heart, Rise to all e - ter - ni - ty.

179

RESTING BY AND BY

The work of the Adventist pioneers was often physically very exhausting. Travel was by horse and buggy in the summer and by sleigh in the winter. Trains and ships were the only means available for travel over longer distances. Microphones were not available to assist the weary speakers when they arose in churches and camp meetings to preach, after having spent the night in an unheated room or tent. It is a wonder that more of them did not become discouraged and disheartened.

W. A. Spicer recalls in his book *Pioneer Days of the Advent Movement*, published in 1941:

"In one General Conference, in the old Battle Creek church—when even the annual session did not bring any great audience to the comparatively small meetinghouse—things were going hard. They were considering a depressing situation. Then cheerfully James White called to his wife, 'Come, Ellen, let us sing for them.' And standing together on the platform, the elder and his wife sang one of the old hymns of everlasting and courageous keeping on [here Spicer quotes the first stanza of "Resting By and By"].

"By the time the first stanza was finished, the spirit of the song was carrying all of them into the chorus [the words are quoted]" (p. 163).

In Ellen White's later years, this is one of the hymns that she sang softly to herself as she went about her work at her Elmshaven home in northern California. Doubtless it encouraged her as she remembered the weary struggles she and her husband, James, had endured during the early days of our church.

"Resting By and By" first appeared in an Adventist hymnal in *Hymns and Spiritual Songs*, published in 1872—the last hymnbook compiled by James White before his death in 1881. The hymn last appeared in *Hymns and Tunes*, first published in 1886.

Resting By and By

Sydney Dyer   Robert Lowry (1826-1899)

1. When faint and wea-ry toil - ing, The sweat-drops on my brow; I
2. This life to toil is giv - en, And he im-proves it best Who
3. Nor ask when, o - ver - burdened, You long for friend-ly aid, "Why
4. Wan reap - er in the har -vest, Let this thy strength sus - tain, Each

long to rest from la - bor, To drop the bur - den now, There
seeks by pa - tient la - bor To en - ter in - to rest; Then
i - dle stands my broth - er, No yoke up - on him laid?" The
sheef that fills the gar - ner Brings you e - ter - nal gain; Then

comes a gen - tle chid - ing, To quell each mourn-ing sigh: "Work
Pil - grim, worn and wea - ry, Press on, the goal is nigh; The
Mas - ter bids him tar - ry, And dare you ask him why? "Go
bear the cross with pa - tience, To fields of du - ty hie; "Tis

while the day is shin - ing; There's rest - ing by and by."
prize is straight be - fore thee There's rest - ing by and by.
la - bor in my vine - yard, There's rest - ing by and by."
sweet to work for Je - sus: There's rest - ing by and by.

Refrain

Rest-ing by and by, There's rest-ing by and by; The shall not al-ways la-bor, We shall not al-ways cry; The end is draw-ing near-er, The end for which we sigh; We'll lay our heav-y bur-dens down; There's rest-ing by and by.

REVIVE US AGAIN

R evive Us Again" was one of the gospel songs that Ella (White) Robinson remembered her grandmother, Ellen G. White, singing during the day as she went about her work. Since at heart Ellen White basically was an evangelist, it is little wonder that this song was among those she liked to sing.

As a girl Ellen had participated in the Millerite revival movement of the 1840s. She, along with thousands of others, found her heart responding to the preaching of William Miller and other Adventist ministers. For the rest of her life, Ellen continued to feel the need of revival and reformation.

In December 1867, James and Ellen White, along with J. N. Andrews, made a visit to the Washington, New Hampshire, Adventist Church. Frederick Wheeler, generally considered to be the first Sabbathkeeping Adventist minister, had moved away sometime earlier; his departure proved a serious loss of leadership to the group in Washington. During the years that followed, confusion and distraction came into that church. The inconsistent course of many of the older members naturally repulsed the children and youth.

William C. White, son of James and Ellen, tells about the revival that took place there during the Christmas of 1867.

"By the time of the visit of Elder and Mrs. White and Elder Andrews in the latter part of December 1867, even the Sabbath school had been discontinued. Those who had made a profession had backslidden, and those who had not were in a condition hard to reach.

"Among the members of the church was a brother [W. H. Ball] who was in active opposition to many of the church tenets. He had written bitter articles of criticism to the papers of other denominations against the church and its doctrines.

"It was evident that little or no benefit could come to the church at Washington until this opposition was met and conquered. . . .

"But the reclamation of Brother [Ball] was not the only victory resulting from the meetings in Washington. Personal testimonies were borne by Mrs. White relating to the shortcomings of several members, and words of encouragement were spoken to others who were doubting their acceptance with God.

"On Monday the meeting began in the morning and continued

183

for more than five hours. During this time one person after another in the congregation was addressed by Sister White.

"Brother and Sister Newell Mead, who 'had been passing through the dark waters' until 'the billows had nearly gone over their heads,' were assured that God loved them, and that 'if they would only trust their ways to Him, He would bring them forth from the furnace of affliction purified.'

"A young sister 'beloved of God, but held in servile bondage,' was counseled that in her married life she must maintain her individuality, and not yield her convictions to follow the will of an unconverted husband.

" 'She did run well for a season; what did hinder her?' was the message of the angel, given through Sister White to another young girl who had departed from God and was enshrouded in darkness. Her backsliding was shown to be due to her association with unconsecrated youth.

"Tender words were addressed to a brother who had been deemed by the church members to be unworthy of membership with them. 'God who sees hearts' had been better pleased with his deportment than with the lives of some who had held him outside.

"And so the personal messages were delivered one by one. At length there came into the mind of a young man [Eugene Farnsworth], nineteen years old, the thought, 'I wish she would tackle the case of my father.' As if in answer to his unspoken wish, Sister White almost immediately addressed the father [William Farnsworth], saying in substance:

" 'I saw that this brother is a slave to tobacco. But the worst of the matter is that he is acting the part of a hypocrite, trying to deceive his brethren into thinking that he has discarded it, as he promised to do when he united with the church.'

"The young man had known by observation that his father was a slave to King Nicotine. As they had worked together in the woods, he had not failed to note the accusing brown stain in the snow where his father expectorated, and had quickly sought to hide the evidence by kicking clean snow over it. This inconsistent course in one who was acting as a leader in the church, together with what he and other youth knew of the faults of others of the older church members, had hardened their hearts against the claims of Christ. Now as he saw these covered sins dealt with faithfully by the servant of the Lord, his heart was struck with conviction that he was witnessing a manifestation of the prophetic gift.

"After the testimonies addressed to various individuals were delivered, opportunity was given for response, and one after another arose and acknowledged the truthfulness of the message, and with repentance and confession yielded himself anew to God.

"During all these meetings, earnest efforts had been put forth by Elder and Mrs. White and by Elder Andrews for the conversion of the children of the Sabbathkeeping families. Now, as the parents made confessions to their children and removed the stumbling blocks from their lives, the youth were tenderly affected.

"At the meeting on Christmas Day, Wednesday forenoon, thirteen of the children and youth arose and expressed a desire to be Christians. Relating an experience of that evening, Orville O. Farnsworth said . . . :

" 'I went with some of my brothers to exchange Christmas gifts with our cousins, Fred and Rose Mead. Because of the meetings the previous evening, we were delayed one day in giving our humble presents to each other. Fred had been a rather wild boy, but he was present in the morning meeting, and he and his sister had taken their stand for Christ. Now they felt a burden for souls, and we were invited into Fred's room, where, after an earnest appeal, we knelt together by his bed, and I gave my heart to the Lord.'

"Four other children who had not been present at the morning meeting also made their surrender in response to appeals from their young friends, making a total of eighteen.

"It was with great rejoicing because God had so abundantly blessed their labors that James and Ellen White left Washington the morning after this memorable Christmas. And how their hearts would have swelled with joy and gratitude to God could they have foreseen the future of this little group of children and youth from the rugged New Hampshire hills. Out of these eighteen new converts, not fewer than nine became workers in the cause of God" (*Review and Herald*, Feb. 11, 1937; see also A. L. White, *Ellen G. White: The Progressive Years*, pp. 216-219).

The gospel song "Revive Us Again" first appeared in a Seventh-day Adventist hymnal in 1886 when it was included in *Hymns and Tunes*. The later, very popular *Christ in Song*, compiled by Frank E. Belden, also included it. The words were written by William Paton Mackay and the tune was composed by J. J. Husband.

Revive Us Again

Hab. 3: 2
William Patton Mackay

J. J. Husband
Arr. from the English

1. We praise Thee, O God, for the Son of Thy love,
2. We praise Thee, O God, for Thy Spir - it of light,
3. All glo - ry and praise to the Lamb that was slain,
4. All glo - ry and praise to the God of all grace,
5. Re - vive us a - gain; fill each heart with Thy love;

For Je - sus who died, and is now gone a - bove.
Who has shown us our Sav - ior, and scat - tered our night.
Who has borne all our sins and has cleansed ev - ery stain.
Who has bought us, and sought us, and guid - ed our ways.
May each soul be re - kin - dled with fire from a - bove.

Refrain

Hal - le - lu - jah! Thine the glo - ry, Hal - le - lu - jah! a - men;

Hal - le - lu - jah! Thine the glo - ry, Re - vive us a - gain.

SMOKING AND CHEWING SONG

In the nineteenth century medical evidence had not yet been discovered to show the harmfulness of smoking. In fact, popular thinking went in quite the opposite direction. John N. Loughborough recalled that in 1850, about two years before he became a Sabbathkeeper, he was advised to use tobacco as a remedy because he was suffering from a slight lung ailment. So he began to smoke cigars to cure his problem! But he gave them up when he started keeping the Sabbath in 1852. He recalled, "One day as I lighted a cigar, the filthiness of the tobacco habit passed before me like a panorama in contrast with the character of those who are to dwell in the New Jerusalem. I heard as distinctly as if a voice had spoken, 'Suppose the Lord should come and find you with that cigar in your mouth. Would you be permitted in that clean place?'

" 'No! Lord, by Thy grace I abandon tobacco forever!' I threw the partly smoked cigar into the Genesee River [which flows through Rochester, New York], and from that day to this never let a particle of the foul stuff pass my lips. The desire for it left me completely" (Adriel Chilson, *Miracles in My Life, Autobiography of Adventist Pioneer J. N. Loughborough*, p. 15).

J. N. Loughborough went on to be an evangelist in the church and was one of the first two ministers to begin the work in California in 1868. He died in 1924 at the age of 92.

As early as about 1848 Ellen White had counseled that tobacco should not be used by Sabbathkeepers. In 1851 she wrote to a Brother Barnes: "I have seen in vision that tobacco was a filthy weed, and that it must be laid aside or given up. Said my accompanying angel, 'If it is an idol, it is high time it was given up, and unless it is given up, the frown of God will be upon the one that uses it, and he cannot be sealed with the seal of the living God. If it is used as a medicine, go to God; He is the Great Physician, and those that use the filthy weed for medicine greatly dishonor God. There is a balm in Gilead, there is a Physician there. Be ye clean that bear the vessels of the Lord' " (letter 5, 1851; quoted in A. L. White, *Ellen G. White: The Early Years*, p. 224).

Ellen White then encouraged the brother to pray in faith, because she understood the struggle that he would probably go through to overcome the habit.

Crusading against the use of both tobacco and alcohol was part of the temperance program supported by the Seventh-day Adventist Church in the nineteenth century. But beyond the moral and physical effects to the user that these habits caused, tobacco smoke especially was a bother to nonusers, such as Adventists, who still were forced to inhale it. In a time before designated nonsmoking areas had come into vogue, having to inhale another's tobacco smoke was a real problem.

To travel between camp meetings and other speaking appointments, Adventist ministers had to spend a great deal of time on trains or sitting in stations awaiting the arrival of the next train. These places often were filled with smoke; it was difficult to get a breath of fresh air. Ellen White comments on such situations in several places in her writings: "We rarely pass through a crowd but men will puff their poisoned breath in our faces. It is unpleasant, if not dangerous, to remain in a railway car or in a room where the atmosphere is impregnated with the fumes of liquor and tobacco" (*Christian Temperance and Bible Hygiene*, pp. 33, 34).

Especially in the early days of the church, James and Ellen White traveled as cheaply as they could because of lack of money. Ellen recalled: "For want of means we took the cheapest private conveyance, second-class [railroad] cars, and lower-deck passage on steamers. . . . When on second-class cars, we were usually enveloped in tobacco smoke, the effects of which often caused me to faint. When on steamers, on lower deck, we suffered the same from the smoke of tobacco, besides the swearing and vulgar conversation of the ship hands and the baser portion of the traveling public" (*Testimonies*, vol. 1, p. 77).

Ellen's desire for fresh air instead of the stale train air she was often forced to endure occasionally got her into trouble with the other passengers. As she was traveling one night, she decided to open the window. She describes what happened: "I raised my window and was enjoying the fresh air, when a lady, in earnest, imploring tones, cried out, 'Do put down that window. You will take cold and be sick, for the night air is so unhealthy.' I replied, 'Madam, we have no other air, in the car or out of it, but night air. If you refuse to breathe night air, then you must stop breathing. God has provided for His creatures air to breathe for the day, and the same, made a little cooler, for the night. . . . The question is: Shall the night air we breathe be pure, or is it improved after it has been breathed over and over? . . . The exhalations thrown off by the lungs and bodies of men steeped in tobacco and alcohol pollute the air and endanger health; and yet nearly all the passengers sit as indifferent as though inhaling the purest atmosphere' " (*Testimonies*, vol. 2, p. 528).

By 1884 Ellen White had already crossed the United States numerous times by train. On a trip across in May of that year, Mrs. White again found herself with a group of people who insisted on smoking. Even after talking to both the train conductor and porter, it was impossible to get the smokers to stop, or for her to find another place on the train to escape their smoke. Since smoking was not allowed at night in the sleepers, the smokers did have to stop for a few hours, but first thing in the morning, they started smoking again. Mrs. White observed, "Close by our seats [they] began their devotion, to offer up their morning sacrifice. To whom—?" (*Ellen G. White Manuscript Releases*, vol. 19, p. 285). Though later the smokers moved elsewhere in the car, their smoke still circulated throughout it.

But it was not just the smoking that they contended with; chewing tobacco was also a problem.

In 1871 the *Health Reformer* reprinted an article from another journal written by a woman who had recently traveled across country by train. She was one who had problems with men and their chewing tobacco:

"The men chew and spit, they read and spit, they talk and spit, they laugh and spit, they breathe and spit, and some—swear and spit.

"Windows were open at the right and left, but they apparently considered it a sin to spit out of them, preferring to make use of the cars. Well, it would have been a pity to sully the fair face of nature; indeed, one might truly compassionate a country drenched in such narcotic showers.

"By lamplight, as by daylight, the process went on. And what a scene did the flickering lights dimly disclose! Men shaken equally out of their starch and out of their dignity, tumbling and rolling every way, some from their horizontal positions spitting now more directly upon their neighbors. Women cuddled up on the seats, evidently ill at ease, and starting even in their slumbers, as well they might amid these threatening showers" (*Health Reformer*, March 1871, p. 198).

Ellen White also commented on the problem caused by the tobacco chewers: "Professed Christians bow before God in their families to pray with their mouths defiled with the filth of tobacco. They go to the house which they have dedicated to God, professing to worship Him, with a stupefying quid of tobacco in their mouths, and the high-colored saliva staining their lips and chin, and their foul breath polluting the atmosphere. They leave their poisonous filth either upon the floor or in receptacles prepared for that purpose. This is the offering they present to God. Instead of the cloud of fragrant incense filling the house as in the case of the ancient tabernacle, it is filled with the sickening, polluted odor of ejected tobacco spittle and quids, and the air breathed by the congregation is poisoned" (*Spiritual Gifts*, vol. 4, p. 127).

Considering the situation Adventists found themselves in, and the emphasis they placed on temperance, it is not surprising that a songbook was brought out in 1880 by the American Health and Temperance Association, under the presidency of John Harvey Kellogg, M.D. *Temperance and Gospel Songs for the Use of Temperance Clubs and Gospel Temperance Meetings* was actually edited by James Edson White, the second son of James and Ellen White.

"Smoking and Chewing Song" apparently was written specifically for the hymnal. It never was reprinted in any other hymnbooks. The 1880 copyright owner is given as J. E. White.

The tune was written by W. J. Bostwick, an Adventist at the time who, unfortunately, later had a drinking problem and eventually died from it. No author is listed for the words.

Smoking and Chewing Song

Anon.

W. J. Bostwick, 1880

Arr. by Sandra G. Gray, 1988

1. Chew-ing in the par - lor, Smok-ing in the street, Chok-ing with ci - gar smoke
2. Pud - dles in the cor - ners, Swell -ing in - to one, Form-ing lakes and riv - ers,
3. Man - y car - ry spi - ces, Cin - a-mon and cloves, Make use of your eye - sight,

Ev - ery one you meet; Spit -ting on the pave-ment, Spit - ing on the floor,
Dry -ing in the sun. Maid- ens nev-er mar - ry Men who smoke or chew!
Make use of your nose; For when you are mar-ried Spice they throw a - way;

Is there such en - slave - ment? Is there such a bore?
If they use to - bac - co, They will nev - er do.
And your lov - ing hus - band Smokes and chews all day.

Refrain

Chew-ing! Smok-ing! Spit-ting! Chok-ing! Send- ing clouds a
Chew-ing! Smok-ing! Spit-ting! Chok-ing!

191

whirl - ing   in   ev - ery - bod - y's face.   Chew - ing in the par - lor,

Spit - ting on the floor,   Is there such en-slave - ment? Is there such a bore?

Used by permission.

SWEET BY AND BY

It was a Sabbath afternoon in 1915 at Ellen White's Elmshaven home near Pacific Union College, in northern California. Several weeks earlier, on February 13, Mrs. White had broken her hip. From then on she was confined to bed or to a wheelchair. Ellen was now well past her eighty-seventh birthday. For more than 70 years she had been used by God to bring messages of hope and encouragement, as well as correction and reproof. Now her long life was nearing its close. Gradually, as the days and weeks passed by, she grew weaker and weaker.

Whenever possible, her family and friends visited her in the large writing room where she had done so much work during the years she lived at Elmshaven. A hospital bed had been brought in for her. On occasion her family and workers would gather around to sing some of her favorite hymns.

On this particular Sabbath, not long before her death, Ellen listened in silence as her family and some friends sang around her bedside. Someone began to sing "There's a land that is fairer than day." As the others picked up the words, they noticed that Mrs. White was also trying to join them. In her weak, trembling voice they heard her sing in little more than a whisper, "We shall sing on that beautiful shore the melodious songs of the blest, and our spirits shall sorrow no more, not a sigh for the blessing of rest."

To those present it almost seemed that in anticipation Ellen White was already singing with the angel choir. A few days later she spoke her last words to her son, W. C. White: "I know in whom I have believed." Her death came at 3:40 p.m. on Friday afternoon, July 16, 1915. With her family and workers once again gathered around her bedside, she quietly breathed her last.

During the five months of Ellen White's final illness, only one vision is recorded as having been given her by God. His last communication through her was to the youth of the church. The message was first printed in the *Review and Herald* of April 15, 1915. (It is reprinted in full in *Messages to Young People*, pp. 287-289, and also *Fundamentals of Christian Education*, pp. 547-549.)

"Sweet By and By" was originally written in 1867. The tune was composed by Joseph Philbrick Webster (1819-1875), and the words were written by Sanford Fillmore Bennett (1836-1898). One day

Webster, a musician with a very sensitive nature and subject to such fits of depression that he would totally ignore even his best friends, came into Bennett's drugstore in Elkhorn, Wisconsin. Being in one of his moods, Webster responded to Bennett's inquiry about what was troubling him by saying, "No matter, it will be all right by and by."

This started Bennett to thinking. Within a short time he had written three stanzas and a refrain. He showed them to Webster. His friend brightened up as he read the words. Webster sat down and wrote the melody. He then asked for a violin so he could play the melody and write the harmony. Within 30 minutes the two men, along with two others who had come into the store, were singing "Sweet By and By" as it is now published.

The hymn made its first appearance in a Seventh-day Adventist hymnal in 1878, when J. E. White included it in his *Song Anchor*.

Sweet By and By

Isa. 33: 24

S. F. Bennett, 1867 (1836-1898)

J. P. Webster, 1867 (1819-1875)

1. There's a land that is fair - er than day, And by faith we can
2. We shall sing on that beau - ti - ful shore The me - lo - di - ous
3. To our boun - ti - ful Fa - ther a - bove, We will of - fer a

see it a - far; For the Fa - ther waits o - ver the way, To pre -
songs of the blest, And our spir - its shall sor - row no more, Not a
trib - ute of praise, For the glo - ri - ous gift of His love, And the

pare us a dwell - ing place there. In the sweet by and
sigh for the bless - ing of rest.
bless - ings that hal - low our days.

In the sweet

by, We shall meet on that beau - ti - ful shore; In the

by and by, by and by,

sweet by and by, We shall meet on that beau - ti - ful shore

In the sweet by and by,

THE COMING KING
IS AT THE DOOR

The promise of Christ's soon return has been the hope of Christians ever since He was here on earth. This hymn and its tune were written by Frank E. Belden, the son of Ellen White's older sister, Sarah. The words are based on Matthew 24:33, 34: "So likewise ye, when ye shall see these things, know that it is near, even at the doors. Verily I say unto you, This generation shall not pass, till all these things be fulfilled." Other texts referred to in the hymn are Matthew 24:3: "What shall be the sign of thy coming, and of the end of the world?"; Matthew 24:6, 7: "Ye shall hear of wars and rumours of wars. . . . For nation shall rise against nation, and kingdom against kingdom"; and 1 Corinthians 15:54: "This mortal shall have put on immortality."

The hymn "The Coming King Is at the Door" was written in 1886 and included in *Hymns and Tunes*, published that year. Frank Belden and Edwin Barnes were the music editors for the hymnal. It was later reprinted in both Belden's popular *Christ in Song* and the 1941 *Church Hymnal*.

Belief in the second coming of Christ was considered so important that the pioneers included it as part of the denominational name, "Seventh-day Adventist," when it was chosen in 1860. Although the Millerite Adventist movement, out of which our church emerged, had fixed on a specific date for Christ's return, Seventh-day Adventists have never done so. Rather, we have constantly felt that it is near, "even at the door."

In the past more than in the present, expressions such as "If time should last . . . ," "If we are still here . . . ," or "If Jesus hasn't returned by then . . ." were commonly heard as Adventists laid future plans—either personal ones or plans for some church project. At many General Conference sessions, delegates have expressed their fervent hope that that would be the last session on earth, and that the next one would be in heaven. Belief in the nearness of Christ's return has been, and should continue to be, uppermost in Adventist thinking.

About 1861 William C. White, third son of James and Ellen White, heard a sermon on the second coming of Christ. He was 7 years old at the time. In 1919 he recalled his reaction to that sermon: "At the Sabbath morning service . . . the preacher had said, 'Only a few more years we have to labor and wait, and then our Lord will come to end our struggle with sin and bring in everlasting righteousness.'

"Going home after the service, I said to my companions, 'How many are a few years?' Edson did not know, but John Foy said, 'Six or seven.' Then I reckoned, 'Seven and seven are 14; it may be that I shall be 14 years old when Christ comes'" (*Review and Herald*, July 31, 1919).

W. C. White lived 76 years beyond the age when as a child he thought Jesus would return. He died in 1937. Decades more have passed, and still Christ has not come. Yet as Christians we are admonished to remember that the time is near, and that we should watch so He does not return and catch us off guard as a thief that comes in the night.

Christ's return was constantly presented to Ellen White in vision as being near, just as it had earlier been presented to the New Testament writers.

In Mrs. White's first book, *A Sketch of the Christian Experience and Views of Ellen G. White*, published in 1851, she wrote:

"Some are looking too far off for the coming of the Lord. Time has continued a few years longer than they expected; therefore they think it may continue a few years more, and in this way their minds are being led from present truth, out after the world. . . . I saw that the time for Jesus to be in the Most Holy Place was nearly finished and that time can last but a very little longer. What leisure time we have should be spent in searching the Bible, which is to judge us in the last day. . . .

"Now is the time, while the four angels are holding the four winds, to make our calling and election sure" (pp. 46, 47; quoted in *Early Writings*, p. 58).

As early as 1883 Ellen White wrote:

"Had Adventists, after the great disappointment in 1844, held fast their faith, and followed on unitedly in the opening providence of God, receiving the message of the third angel and in the power of the Holy Spirit proclaiming it to the world, they would have seen the salvation of God, the Lord would have wrought mightily with their efforts, the work would have been completed, and Christ would have come ere this to receive His people to their reward" (*Selected*

197

Messages, book 1, p. 68).

Although Christ might have come sooner, but has not, Ellen White also wrote encouragingly, "The coming of the Lord is nearer than when we first believed. The great controversy is nearing its end. Every report of calamity by sea or land is a testimony to the fact that the end of all things is at hand. Wars and rumors of wars declare it. Is there a Christian whose pulse does not beat with quickened action as he anticipates the great events opening before us?" (*Evangelism*, p. 219).

The promise is sure. It cannot fail; for Christ Himself said, "I will come again" (John 14:3). So today, Adventists join with the apostle John, who prayed, "Even so, come, Lord Jesus" (Rev. 22:20).

The Coming King Is at the Door

Matt. 24:33, 34

EVEN AT THE DOOR

F. E. Belden, 1886 (1858-1945)

F. E. Belden, 1886

1. The com - ing King is at the door, Who once the cross for sinners bore,
2. The signs that show His com-ing near Are fast ful - fill-ing year by year,
3. Look not on earth for srtife to cease, Look not be -low for joy and peace,
4. Then in the glo-rious earth made new We'll dwell the countless a -ges through;

But now the righ - teous ones a - lone, He comes to gath - er home.
And soon we'll hail the glo-rious dawn Of heaven's e - ter - nal morn.
Un - til the Sav - ior comes a - gain To ban - ish death and sin.
This mor - tal shall im - mor - tal be, And time, e - ter - ni - ty.

At the door, at the door, At the door, yes, e-ven at the door;

At the door, at the door,

He is com - ing, He is com - ing, He is e - ven at the door.

com-ing a - gain, com-ing a -gain,

199

THERE IS SUNLIGHT
ON THE HILLTOP

T
here Is Sunlight on the Hilltop" was among several of Ellen White's favorite hymns, according to her oldest granddaughter, Ella (White) Robinson. During her later years, when it was not easy for her to exercise, she liked to take a horse-and-buggy ride for an hour or so each day. Ella sometimes accompanied her grandmother on those rides. This is one of the songs that Ella remembered her grandmother singing as they rode down the country lanes to the accompaniment of the horses' hooves. Ella also recalled that often as they rode along, Ellen White would comment as they passed a house, "Do you suppose the family living in that house has heard the glorious message of Jesus' coming?"

If Mrs. White happened to see people out in their yard, she would stop and talk with them. Sometimes she would share some produce from her garden or fruit from her trees that she had brought along expressly for such a purpose. For years after Ellen White moved back to the United States from Australia in 1900, as well as long after her death in 1915 at her Elmshaven home in northern California, her former neighbors fondly remembered the little old woman who came around in her buggy and talked so lovingly of Jesus.

Although morning worships at Ellen White's home were generally short, evening worships were not to be rushed. Especially on Friday evenings there was time for the singing of several hymns before Ellen White read from the Bible. (For a description of Friday evening worships, see under "Safely Through Another Week.") Ellen liked songs that were upbeat, and talked about progress in our Christian experience.

Mrs. White did not like to see sad, long-faced people. She did not think such people properly represented their Christian religion. She had no use for sour piety, as she called it. On one occasion when she saw her granddaughter Ella looking quite downcast, she said to her, "Ella May, if you could think a person who apparently had nothing to be thankful for—no friends, no money, perhaps was suffering from an incurable disease, and owned nothing of any material value in the world—yet the plan of salvation and the promise of a glorious future, aren't they sufficient to keep that person singing from morning 'til night?"

In describing music as a weapon against discouragement, Ellen White wrote, "If there was much more praising the Lord, and far less doleful recitation of discouragements, many more victories would be achieved" (*Evangelism*, p. 499).

Another time she wrote, "Song is a weapon that we can always use against discouragement. As we thus open the heart to the sunlight of the Saviour's presence, we shall have health and His blessing" (*The Ministry of Healing*, p. 254).

It appears that "There Is Sunlight on the Hilltop" was one of Ellen White's favorite weapons against discouragement. This hymn by Mrs. M. T. Haughey was copyrighted in 1886 by Frank E. Belden and first appeared in *Hymns and Tunes*, published that same year. The tune was also composed by Mrs. Haughey.

There Is Sunlight on the Hilltop

Ps. 9: 1

Mrs. M. T. Haughey

M. T. Haughey; arr.

1. There is sun-light on the hill-top, There is sun-light on the sea;
2. In the dust I leave my sad-ness, As the garb of oth-er days;
3. Lov-ing Sav-ior, Thou hast bought me, And my life, my all is Thine;

And the gold-en beams are sleep-ing, On the soft and ver-dant lea;
For Thou rob-est me with glad-ness, And Thou fill-est me with praise;
Let the lamp Thy love hath light-ed To Thy praise and glo-ry shine;

But a rich-er light is fill-ing All the cham-bers of my heart;
And to that bright home of glo-ry Which Thy love hath won for me,
And to that bright home of glo-ry Which Thy love hath won for me.

For Thou dwell-est there, my Sav-ior, And 'tis sun-light where Thou art.
In my heart and mind as-cend-ing, My glad spir-it fol-lows Thee.
In my heart and mind as-cend-ing, My glad spir-it fol-lows Thee.

O the sun-light! beau-ti -ful sun-light! O the sun - light in the heart!

Je - sus' smile can ban -ish sad - ness, It is sun - light in the heart.

THERE WERE NINETY AND NINE

Among the hymns that Ellen White's oldest granddaughter, Ella M. (White) Robinson, specifically recalled hearing her grandmother sing was "There Were Ninety and Nine." Mrs. White often sang as she moved about her home doing her work during the day. Ella recalled the tender pathos in her grandmother's voice as Ellen sang this song, especially the third stanza:

But none of the ransomed ever knew
   How deep were the waters crossed,
Nor how dark was the night that the Lord passed through,
   Ere He found His sheep that was lost.
Far out in the desert He heard its cry—
   Fainting and helpless and ready to die,
   Fainting and helpless and ready to die.

Among Ellen White's favorite topics was Jesus Christ. *The Desire of Ages*, her biography of Christ, which she worked on for several years, was published in 1898. One of its chapters was entitled "The Divine Shepherd." The book was an expansion of *Spirit of Prophecy*, volumes 2 and 3, which had been published in 1877 and 1878. As she was expanding her work on the life of Christ in 1892, she wrote to O. A. Olsen, president of the General Conference:

"This week I have been enabled to commence writing on the life of Christ. Oh, how inefficient, how incapable I am of expressing the things which burn in my soul in reference to the mission of Christ! I have hardly dared to enter upon the work. There is so much to it all. . . . I lie awake at nights.

"I walk with trembling before God. I know not how to speak or trace with pen the large subject of the atoning sacrifice. I know not how to present the subjects in the living power in which they stand before me. I tremble for fear lest I shall belittle the great plan of salvation by cheap words. I bow my soul in awe and reverence before God and say, 'Who is sufficient for these things?' " (letter 40, 1892; quoted in A. L. White, *Ellen G. White: The Australian Years*, p. 382).

Although in her writings and talks Ellen White often used illustrations from things she saw and experienced in life, apparently she never watched sheep as a girl—so she could not relate directly to the work of a shepherd. However, it had been her duty to tend the family milk cow. This story from her childhood shows that she knew from personal experience what it was to look for something that was lost:

"One evening as she went to the pasture gate to bring the cow to the shed for milking, the bossy that usually was there waiting for her was nowhere in sight. Ellen went down through the woods, frequently calling the cow. Not until she had reached a little brook in the valley below did she hear a response. To her dismay she found the cow in the middle of the stream, with all four feet stuck in the mud. Immediately Ellen set about devising a plan to get the cow unstuck. Picking some luscious grass nearby, she reached out to the cow, who was grateful for something to eat. After repeating this several times, Ellen offered the cow another generous handful of grass, but this time held it just a little beyond her reach. Then with her free hand grasping the nearest horn, Ellen urged, 'Come, Bossy,' and moved the grass away. The cow, fearful of losing the promised morsel, put forth extraordinary effort to break loose from the mud. Soon Ellen and cow were making their way back to home and shed" (A. L. White, *Ellen G. White: The Early Years*, p. 20).

Throughout her life, concern for the salvation of souls was a primary motivation for Ellen White. Having herself experienced the joy of salvation, she wanted others to have the same opportunity. It is little wonder that the hymn "There Were Ninety and Nine" with its message of salvation, even for the one lost sheep, was popular with Mrs. White.

The first Seventh-day Adventist hymnal that included this hymn was the original edition of *Christ in Song*, published in 1900. In that edition F. E. Belden wrote his own tune for the words. When the second and expanded edition of *Christ in Song* came out in 1908, it used the original tune by Ira Sankey. The hymn was also included in the 1941 *Church Hymnal*.

The words to the hymn were written by Elizabeth C. Clephane (1830-1869) and first published in 1868 in *The Children's Hour*. They were reprinted in 1874 in the *Christian Age*, where they caught the attention of Ira Sankey (1840-1908), who was Dwight L. Moody's singing evangelist. The two men were traveling at the time by train from Glasgow to Edinburgh. Sankey read the poem to Moody, but the great evangelist did not show much interest in it. At Moody's second evangelistic meeting in Edinburgh, his topic was "The Good

Shepherd." He asked Sankey to sing a solo after the sermon.

As Ira Sankey sat at the piano wondering what he should sing, it seemed as though a voice said to him, "Sing the hymn you found on the train." With a silent prayer for help, Sankey put the newspaper clipping on the piano and began to play. As he sang, the tune came to him note by note. By the time he had completed singing and playing the first two stanzas, the tune was fixed in his mind, and has remained unchanged since that night.

There Were Ninety and Nine

Luke 15: 7

Elizabeth C. Clephane (1830-1869)

Ira D. Sankey (1840-1908)

1. There were nine - ty and nine that safe - ly lay In the
2. "Lord, Thou hast here Thy nine - ty and nine; Are they
3. But none of the ran - somed ev - er knew How
4. "Lord, whence are these blood - drops all the way That
5. But all through the moun - tains, thun - der - riv'n, And

shel - ter of the fold, But one was out on the
not e - nough for Thee?" But the Shep-herd made an - swer,
deep were the wa - ters crossed, Nor how dark was the night that the
mark out the moun-tain's track?" "They were shed for one who had
up from the rock - y steep, There rose a cry to the

hills a - way, Far, far from the gates of gold--
"One of Mine Has wan - dered a - way from me,
Lord passed through Ere He found His sheep that was lost.
gone a - stray, Ere the Shep - herd could bring him back."
gate of heaven, "Re - joice, I have found my sheep!"

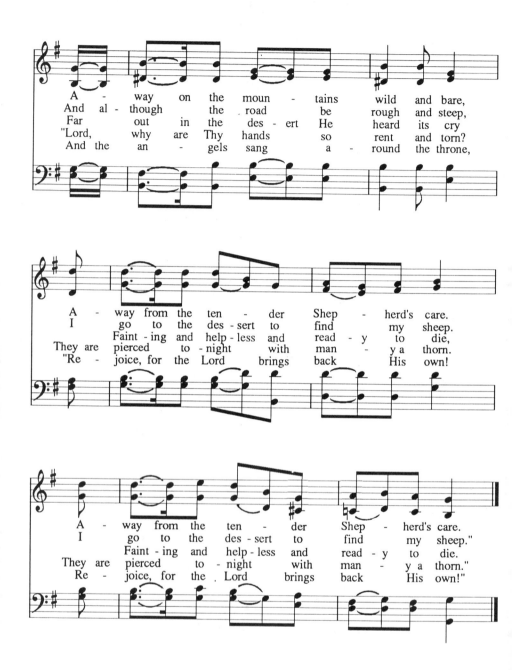

A - way on the moun - tains wild and bare,
And al - though the road be rough and steep,
Far out in the des - ert He heard its cry
"Lord, why are Thy hands so rent and torn?
And the an - gels sang a - round the throne,

A - way from the ten - der Shep - herd's care.
I go to the des - ert to find my sheep.
Faint - ing and help - less and read - y to die,
They are pierced to - night with man - y a thorn.
"Re - joice, for the Lord brings back His own!

A - way from the ten - der Shep - herd's care.
I go to the des - ert to find my sheep."
Faint - ing and help - less and read - y to die.
They are pierced to - night with man - y a thorn."
Re - joice, for the Lord brings back His own!"

208

'TIS LOVE THAT
MAKES US HAPPY

Frank E. Belden, the prolific hymn-writing son of Ellen White's older sister, Sarah, first published this song in 1892 in his *Bible Object Lessons and Songs for Little Ones*, book 1, which he coauthored with Lillie E. Affolter. Although not produced by a Seventh-day Adventist publishing house, this was the first volume of a planned series of three books, each to contain 52 Bible lessons, plus hymns written by Belden to accompany the lessons.

" ' 'Tis Love That Makes Us Happy" was used to illustrate the story of the good Samaritan. After telling the story, the following picture and illustration accompanied the song:

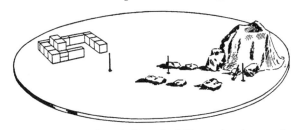

"Note—Teach carefully the golden rule. Direct the children to place the mountain, and then the rocks to mark the rough, dangerous way. Next let them walk the stick along representing the man who fell among thieves; and when telling of his bruises, lean him carefully against a rock. The priest is walked past, and left standing at a distance. Then the Levite is taken past, and the Samaritan comes after. The donkey should not be represented. Direct the children in building the inn, and afterward let them take the good Samaritan and the wounded man there" (Lillie E. Affolter and F. E. Belden, *Bible Object Lessons and Songs for Little Ones*, book 1, pp. 104, 105).

Frank Belden was the first Seventh-day Adventist musician to write hymns specifically for children. He included " ' 'Tis Love That Makes Us Happy" in his *Christ in Song*, which first appeared in 1900 and was revised and expanded in 1908. Though other hymnals did contain a few songs for children, it was not until 1926 when *Sunshine Songs for Boys and Girls* was put out by the editorial department of *Our Little Friend* that the church actually began in earnest to publish songbooks designed for its children. This marked a gap of more than 70 years since Anna White, James White's sister, had compiled our first children's hymnal, *Hymns for Youth and Children*, in 1854. In 1931 *Junior Song Book* was published, and *Joyful Songs for Boys and Girls* in 1932.

Another children's song that F. E. Belden wrote the tune as well as one of the stanzas for is "Like a Little Candle," copyrighted in 1894. It is found in *Christ in Song*, 1908 edition, No. 501.

'Tis Love That Makes Us Happy

F. E. Belden, 1892

F. E. Belden (1858-1945)

1. 'Tis love that makes us hap-py, 'Tis love that smooths the way;
2. This world is full of sor-row, Of sick-ness, death, and sin;
3. And when this life is o-ver, And we are called a-bove

It helps us mind, it makes us kind To oth-ers ev-ery day.
With lov-ing heart we'll do our part, And try some soul to win.
Our song shall be, e-ter-nal-ly, Of Je-sus and His love.

Refrain

God is love; we're His lit-tle chil-dren. God is love; we would be like Him. 'Tis love that makes us hap-py, 'Tis love that smooths the way; It helps us "mind," it makes us kind to oth-ers ev-ery day.

WE KNOW NOT THE TIME
WHEN HE COMETH

On April 20, 1879, this stirring Advent hymn was sung at the dedication of the Dime Tabernacle in Battle Creek, Michigan. The local newspaper reported that it was sung with "charming effect by the choir, and all the congregation who had books."

About a year earlier, James White had called for the building of a church in Battle Creek that would seat 3,000 people. Prior to this, three wood-frame Adventist meetinghouses had already been erected there—each larger than the previous one. The first had been built in 1855. Measuring only 18' x 24', it seated 40 people and cost $300.

By 1857 the congregation had outgrown the first meetinghouse, so they sold it and built a larger one that measured 28' x 42'. It was in this second church that the name Seventh-day Adventist was chosen in 1860 and the General Conference was organized in 1863.

By 1866 the congregation had continued to grow, so a still larger church was needed. It measured 44' x 65' and could seat between 500 and 600 people. In 1878, the year James White called for the building of a still larger church, the denomination's membership had grown from 3,500 in 1863 when the General Conference was organized to 13,077. White felt a church was needed that was not only large enough to hold the growing membership of people affiliated with the publishing house, sanitarium, and college there in Battle Creek, but could also serve for large church meetings such as General Conference sessions.

Work on the new building began on August 20, 1878. James White suggested a novel idea for fund-raising. It was urged that every Adventist give a dime a month for a year to pay for its construction—hence the name "Dime" Tabernacle. The new building was designed to seat 3,200 and contained a 108-foot-high bell and clock tower. The local community suggested the idea of a clock and contributed more than $1,000 to pay for it. The total cost of the building came to $26,275.17, or $1.92 per square foot for the 105 x 130-foot building.

Dedication day dawned bright and beautiful. James and Ellen White decided not to come for the service. He was organizing a wagon train from Texas to Kansas at the time, after which the Whites were scheduled to attend the Kansas camp meeting in May. Their absence did not dampen the enthusiasm of the Battle Creek citizens who came out, an estimated 5,000 strong, to attend the opening service at 2:30 on Sunday afternoon. By actual count, only 3,649 got into the building; the rest milled around outside.

After the singing of a couple hymns, including "We Know Not the Time When He Cometh," followed by prayer and a report from the finance committee, a short history of Seventh-day Adventists was given by Uriah Smith. J. N. Andrews presented the dedication sermon. At the time he was serving as our first official overseas missionary, but had come home to attend the General Conference session of 1878 as well as to look after his daughter Mary's health. She died on November 27, 1878.

Andrews took his texts from the mottoes on the three windows behind the pulpit. Beneath each was painted a Scripture text. The left window had Romans 3:24: "Being justified freely by his grace through the redemption that is in Christ Jesus"; the center window had Exodus 20:3-17: the Ten Commandments; and the right window had Revelation 14:12: "Here are they that keep the commandments of God, and the faith of Jesus." As Andrews pointed out, these texts summarize the law and the gospel.

Some questioned the necessity of having to build such a large structure. The *Advent Review and Sabbath Herald* published an editorial responding to the "don't believers" who had been against organization, systematic benevolence, large publishing houses with power presses, camp meetings, a health institute, and the founding of the college. The editor observed that if the "don't believers" were fortunate enough to make it to heaven, they would probably look around and say, "We don't believe in such a big crowd."

The Dime Tabernacle served the church very well for nearly 43 years until it burned on January 7, 1922. Both James and Ellen White's funerals were held in it, as was the important reorganization General Conference session of 1901—not to mention many other church meetings during those years.

"We Know Not the Time When He Cometh" first appeared in a Seventh-day Adventist hymnal in 1878 when James Edson White included it in his *Song Anchor*. It indicated that the words were written by "S.M.H." and the tune was composed by Will H. Pontius. Although the hymn was later republished in *Hymns and Tunes* in

1886, in *Christ in Song* at the turn of the century, and in the 1941 *Church Hymnal,* none cite the author of the words with anything more than the designation "S.M.H." Whoever the hymn's author was, the message of "waiting and watching" for the Lord's return accurately depicts what Christ told His followers to do until He returns.

We Know Not the Time When He Cometh

Luke 12: 35-37
S. M. H.

WAITING AND WATCHING
Will H. Pontius (1860- ?)

1. We know not the time when He com - eth At e - ven, or midnight or morn; It may be at deep - en - ing twi - light; It may be at ear - li - est dawn. He bids us to watch and be read - y, Nor suf - fer our lights to grow dim, That

2. I think of His won - der - ful pit - y, The price our sal - va-tion hath cost; He left the bright man-sions of glo - ry To suf - fer and die for the lost. And sometimes I think it will please Him, When those whom He died to re - deem Re -

3. O Je -sus, my lov - ing Re - deem - er, Thou know-est I cher-ish as dear The hope that mine eyes shall be - hold Thee, That I shall Thine own wel - come hear! If to some as a judge Thou ap - pear - est, Who forth from Thy pres - ence would flee, A

when He shall come, He may find us All wait - ing and watch-ing for
joice in the hope of His com - ing By wait - ing and watch-ing for
Friend most be - lov - ed I'll greet Thee, I'm wait - ing and watch-ing for

Refrain

Him.
Him.
Thee.

Wait - ing and watch - ing,
Wait -ing and watch-ing, yes, wait - ing for Thee,

Wait - ing and watch - ing; Wait - ing and
Wait -ing and watching, yes, wait - ing for Thee; Wait -ing and watching, yes,

watch - ing, Still wait - ing and watch - ing for Thee.
wait - ing and watching,

WE SHALL MEET BEYOND THE RIVER

This hymn was used to close two of Ellen White's three funerals: the first, held on Sunday afternoon, July 18, 1915, on the lawn in front of her Elmshaven home in northern California; and the third, held Sabbath morning, July 24, 1915, in the Dime Tabernacle in Battle Creek, Michigan. (The second service was held at the camp meeting in progress at Richmond, California.) According to Ellen White's autobiography, *Life Sketches*, the hymn "We Shall Meet Beyond the River" was one of her favorites.

The comforting message of the hymn was echoed in George B. Starr's last visit with Ellen White. On Sunday, June 27, Starr and his wife went to Elmshaven to say goodbye to their longtime friend. In fact, during his brief remarks at the Elmshaven funeral just three weeks later, Starr mentioned that last visit with Mrs. White.

In a letter written June 27, 1915, the very day of the Starrs' visit, W. C. White told about Elder and Mrs. Starr's short conversation with Mrs. White. Mrs. White told the Starrs how pleased she was to have them come see her, and Elder Starr commented on how bright and cheerful she seemed. She replied: " 'I am glad that you find me thus. I have not had many mournful days.'

" 'No,' Brother Starr remarked, 'not in all your life.'

" 'No,' she continued, 'the Lord has arranged and led in all these things for me, and I am trusting in Him. He knows when it will end.'

" 'Yes,' they replied, 'it will soon end and we shall meet you in the kingdom of God, and we will "talk it all over there together," as you wrote us in one of your last letters.'

" 'Oh, yes,' she replied. 'It seems almost too good to be true, but it is true!'" (letter printed in A. L. White, *Ellen G. White, The Later Elmshaven Years*, p. 430).

"We Shall Meet Beyond the River" first appeared in *Pearly Portals: for the Sabbath School*, compiled in 1882 by D. S. Hakes. He wrote the tune for the hymn, and Mrs. E. W. Sawyer is listed as the author. Not much is known about either person. The hymn was also included in *Hymns and Tunes*, first published in 1886. It has not been included in subsequent Adventist hymnals.

We Shall Meet Beyond the River

Rev. 21: 4
Mrs. E. W. Sawyer

D. S. Hakes

1. We shall meet be - yond the riv - er, In that glo - rious land of bliss,
2. We shall meet with those de - part - ed From this world of sin and strife,
3. We shall meet with Christ our Sav - ior. Soon to come and take His own;

Where the Son shall reign for - ev - er As the king of right-teous -ness;
Meet no long - er brok - en heart - ed, But with an e - ter - nal life.
Then we'll share His bless -ed fav - or, And shall know as we are known;

We shall meet in yon-der cit - y, With its walls of jas - per, bright,
We shall meet and share the glo - ry Of that count - less, hap-py throng;
O the joy, the ex - ul - ta - tion Of the saints then tru - ly His!

We shall shout our songs of tri - umph, No more sor - row, pain, nor night.
We shall tell re - demp-tions's sto - ry, Sing His prais - es, loud and long.
O the glo -rious trans - for - ma - tion When we see Him as He is.

Refrain

rit.

We shall meet in yon-der cit - y By and by, and by and by;

We shall sing our songs for - ev - er Round our Sav-ior's throne on high.

YIELD NOT TO TEMPTATION

Both the words and tune for this temperance hymn were written in 1868. It was first published in an Adventist hymnal in 1880 in *Temperance and Gospel Songs*, edited by James Edson White (1849-1928), the second son of James and Ellen White. He produced his temperance songbook for the American Health and Temperance Association of Battle Creek, Michigan. The hymn continued to be published in major Adventist hymnals through the 1941 *Church Hymnal*.

The American Health and Temperance Association had been formed on January 5, 1879, with Dr. John Harvey Kellogg, medical superintendent of the Battle Creek Sanitarium, as its first president. At the organizational meeting some 133 persons signed the teetotaler's pledge, promising to discard the use of tea and other stimulants and narcotics, as well as alcohol. Another 22 signed just the anti-rum and tobacco pledge.

On November 24, 1879, the General Conference voted that it is "the duty of all members of this denomination to become members of the American Health and Temperance Association, and to use their influence in inducing others to unite in this reformatory effort." The dues were set at 25 cents for the first year and 10 cents minimum per year thereafter. Along with the first year's membership came a large certificate suitable for framing. Members were expected to sign one of the following pledges:

TEETOTAL PLEDGE—I do hereby solemnly affirm that with the help of God I will wholly abstain from the voluntary use, as a beverage, or in any equivalent manner, of alcohol, tea, and coffee, and from the use of tobacco, opium, and all other narcotics and stimulants.

ANTI-RUM AND TOBACCO PLEDGE—I do hereby solemnly affirm that with the help of God I will wholly abstain from the voluntary use of alcohol in any form, as a beverage, or in any equivalent manner, and from smoking, chewing, or snuffing tobacco, or using it in any other form, and from in any way encouraging the use of these poisons.

ANTI-WHISKEY PLEDGE—I do hereby solemnly affirm that with the help of God I will totally abstain from the voluntary use, as a beverage, or in any equivalent manner, of all liquids or substances containing alcohol.

Ministers were encouraged to support the program by engaging in health and temperance work. The publication in 1880 of *Temperance and Gospel Songs* was part of this effort.

By 1881 the American Health and Temperance Association had 9,819 members. At the same time the church membership stood at only 16,916. In 1889 the organization was renamed the International Health and Temperance Association.

Temperance has long been advocated among Seventh-day Adventists. Even before Ellen White's first health reform vision of June 1863, in fact, as early as 1848, she had been shown the evils of using tobacco, tea, and coffee.

But even earlier, Joseph Bates, one of the cofounders of the Seventh-day Adventist Church, had been a temperance reformer. In 1821, while still a sailor and several years before even becoming a Christian, he gave up drinking ardent spirits. The following year he resolved to drink no wine and soon afterward also gave up smoking and chewing tobacco, as well as the use of profane language. Before 1838 he had abandoned the use of tea and coffee.

In 1843, the year that as a Millerite Joseph Bates first expected to see the Lord return, he discontinued the use of flesh foods. Bates had already stopped using butter, grease, cheese, pies, rich cakes, and spices. So, long before God first showed Ellen White the harmful effects of unhealthful living, Joseph Bates was already an enthusiastic supporter of the idea. It is interesting, though, that he did not try to dictate to others how they should live. However, after Ellen's vision on the subject, Bates wholeheartedly supported what she had been shown.

Just a month before his death on March 19, 1872, Joseph Bates wrote to Ellen White explaining an incident that had once occurred at a church picnic: "The tables were soon up and loaded with tempting eatables; and I was invited to ask the blessing. The swine's flesh upon the table, I knew was abominable and unclean from creation . . . and God has positively, by law, forbidden the eating or touching of it. . . . I therefore very quietly distinguished, and asked a blessing on the clean, nutritious, wholesome, *lawful* food. Some whispered, and some smiled, and others looked on, and so on" (Godfrey T. Anderson, *Outrider of the Apocalypse*, p. 116).

Yield Not to Temptation

I Cor. 10: 13

Horatio R. Palmer, 1868 (1834-1907)

Horatio R. Palmer, 1868

1. Yield not to temp - ta - tion, For yield-ing is sin, Each vic -t'ry will
2. Shun ev - il com - pan - ions, Bad language dis-dain, God's name hold in
3. To him that o'er - com - eth God giv -eth a crown, Thro' faith we shall

help you Some oth - er to win; Fight man - ful - ly on - ward,
rev-erence, Nor take it in vain; Be thought-ful and ear - nest,
con - quer, Though oft -en cast down; He who is our Sav - ior

Dark pas-sions sub-due,
Kind-heart - ed and true, Look ev-er to Je - sus, He'll car-ry you through.
Our strength will re -new,

Refrain

Ask the Sav - ior to help you, Com - fort, strengthen, and keep you;

He is will - ing to aid you, He will car - ry you through.

221

INDEX